GREAT UNDERSEA ADVENTURES

By the same editors

Great Adventures in Nursing
Great Adventures in Science
The Great Explorers
The New Treasury of Science (with Harlow Shapley)
The Amazing World of Medicine
The New York University Library of Science

GREAT UNDERSEA ADVENTURES

Edited by

HELEN WRIGHT

and

SAMUEL RAPPORT

HARPER & ROW, PUBLISHERS
NEW YORK

GREAT UNDERSEA ADVENTURES

FIRST EDITION

FQ

LIBRARY OF CONGRESS CATALOG CARD NUMBER: 66–18652

Acknowledgments

The editors acknowledge with thanks permission to use the following material:

MENFISH by Captain J. Y. Cousteau with Frédéric Dumas, from "Menfish" in *The Silent World* by Captain J. Y. Cousteau with Frédéric Dumas. Copyright 1953 by Harper & Row, Publishers, Incorporated.

THE BENDS by Captain Edward Ellsberg, reprinted by permission of Dodd, Mead & Company from *Men Under the Sea* by Edward Ellsberg. Copyright 1939 by Edward Ellsberg.

AN EFFORT OF GENIUS by Wilbur Cross, from *Challengers of the Deep* by Wilbur Cross, copyright © 1959 by Wilbur Cross, by permission of William Sloane Associates.

ABOARD A NUCLEAR SUB by Commander James Calvert, from *Surface at the Pole* by James Calvert. Copyright © 1960, Commander James Calvert, U.S.N. Used by permission of McGraw-Hill Book Company.

SEVEN MILES DOWN by Jacques Piccard and Robert S. Dietz, from *Seven Miles Down* by Jacques Piccard and Robert S. Dietz. Copyright © 1961 by Jacques Piccard and Robert S. Dietz. Reprinted by permission of G. P. Putnam's Sons.

THE SECRET NAVAL DISASTER by David Masters, from *Epics of Salvage* by David Masters, by permission of Little, Brown and Co. and the Executors of David Masters. Copyright 1952, 1953 by David Masters.

ORPHAN SHIPS by Jake Jacobs, reprinted by permission

of Dodd, Mead & Company from *Marineland Diver* by Jake Jacobs. Copyright © 1960 by Harold J. and Sylvia Jacobs.

THE WARSHIP *Vasa* RETURNS FROM THE SEA by Robert Silverberg, reprinted with permission from *Sunken History* by Robert Silverberg. Copyright © 1963 by the author. Chilton Books, Philadelphia and New York.

THE PATTERN OF THE SURFACE and THE BIRTH OF AN ISLAND by Rachel Carson, from *The Sea Around Us* by Rachel L. Carson. Copyright © 1950, 1951, 1960 by Rachel L. Carson. Reprinted by permission of Oxford University Press, Inc.

SHARK! PATTERN OF ATTACK by Thomas Helm, reprinted by permission of Dodd, Mead & Company from *Shark!* by Thomas Helm. Copyright © 1961 by Thomas Helm.

ULYSSES AND OTHERS by Captain J. Y. Cousteau with James Dugan, from "The Trucial Reef" in *The Living Sea* by Captain J. Y. Cousteau with James Dugan. Copyright © 1963 by Harper & Row, Publishers, Incorporated. Reprinted by permission of Harper & Row, Publishers.

THE SHAPE OF THE SEA by Arthur C. Clarke, from *The Challenge of the Sea* by Arthur C. Clarke. Copyright © 1960 by Arthur C. Clarke. Reprinted by permission of Holt, Rinehart and Winston, Inc.

CATASTROPHIC WAVES FROM THE SEA by Francis P. Shepard, from *The Earth Beneath the Sea* by Francis P. Shepard. Copyright © 1959 by The Johns Hopkins Press and used with their permission.

CONTENTS

Part 3

Life Undersea

Part 4

Adventures in Oceanography

PREFACE

HAVE YOU ever wished that, like Captain Nemo, hero of Jules Verne's *Twenty Thousand Leagues Under the Sea*, you could range under the oceans in a craft that you commanded? Or that you could encounter great sea monsters, make friends with a grouper, watch an island being born, or plunge into the great abyss of the Challenger Deep? Perhaps someday you will experience such adventures firsthand. Perhaps you will be among the explorers who study the contours of the bottom or raise a sunken ship filled with archaeological treasure. Possibly you many invent some device to penetrate the sea's hidden mysteries. Meanwhile you can share in the exploits of men who have done these things, thrill to the excitement of their discoveries, learn how they have planned and struggled and succeeded, and how in so doing they have opened up a hitherto inaccessible world. To guide you on the voyage is the purpose of this book.

In its pages you will encounter sandhogs, human torpedoes, men suddenly attacked by the bends, the crew of a nuclear submarine, and fishermen sucked down by a whirlpool. Here you will learn something of what science has discovered about the great chasms of the oceans, the tidal waves which have claimed thousands of lives, and the cataclysmic forces that are reshaping the ocean floor. There is much to learn—only recently have we begun to substitute facts for legends about what takes place beneath the waves. Not too long ago men were confined to surface exploration, unable to go very far above or below the earth and its waters. That day is gone, and this book is your introduction to one of the new worlds that men are conquering.

THE EDITORS

Part 1

Going Down: Free Diving to Bathyscaphe

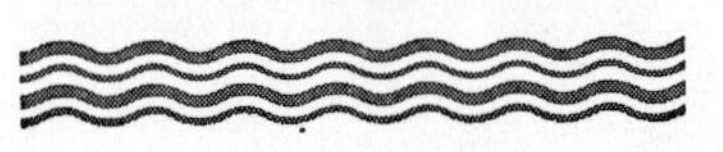

Menfish

by

Captain J. Y. Cousteau

with Frédéric Dumas

From earliest antiquity the world beneath the sea has exerted a fascination on men. With little or no knowledge of the facts, they have peopled it with mermaids, with fabulous monsters, even with hidden colonies in which strange creatures dwelled. A few human beings, seeking a livelihood, have ventured below. As early as the days of Homer, about 1000 B.C.*, naked divers combed the bottom of the sea for sponges and oysters. For centuries the practice has continued and even today, with only the simplest equipment, these divers perform astonishing feats of strength and endurance. Captain Cousteau describes the case of a sixty-year-old Arab sponge fisherman who "without breathing apparatus . . . reached one hundred and thirty feet, in an immersion time of two and one-half minutes." The rec-*

ord is remarkable, but many such divers, unaware of scientific methods of controlling the disease, become crippled by the bends.

Even in ancient times, divers used tubes to suck air down from the surface. Later they used watertight suits of metal or leather. It was not until the nineteenth century that the rigid metal helmet fed by an air pump was invented. Now the helmet is attached to a rubber suit, but the air hose severely limits the diver's freedom of movement. It is from this handicap that the underwater explorer has at length been freed by a remarkable invention called the aqualung. With it he can range about almost with the freedom of a fish. His expeditions may be fraught with dangers, which will be described in later chapters, but the aqualung has opened a whole new world to thousands of sportsmen. How it was first used is described below by the men responsible for its development.

ONE MORNING in June, 1943, I went to the railway station at Bandol on the French Riviera and received a wooden case expressed from Paris. In it was a new and promising device, the result of years of struggle and dreams, an automatic compressed-air diving lung conceived by Émile Gagnan and myself. I rushed it to Villa Barry where my diving comrades, Philippe Tailliez and Frédéric Dumas waited. No children ever opened a Christmas present with more excitement than ours when we unpacked the first "aqualung." If it worked, diving could be revolutionized.

We found an assembly of three moderate-sized cylinders of compressed air, linked to an air regulator the size of an alarm clock. From the regulator there extended two tubes, joining on a mouthpiece. With this equipment harnessed to the back, a watertight glass mask over the eyes and nose, and rubber foot fins, we intended to make unencumbered flights in the depths of the sea.

We hurried to a sheltered cove which would conceal our activity from curious bathers and Italian occupation troops. I checked the air pressure. The bottles contained air condensed to one hundred and fifty times atmospheric pressure. It was difficult to contain my excitement and discuss calmly the plan of the first dive. Dumas, the best goggle diver in France, would stay on shore keeping warm and rested, ready to dive to my aid, if necessary. My wife, Simone, would swim out on the surface with a schnorkel breathing tube and watch me through her submerged mask. If she signaled anything had gone wrong, Dumas could dive to me in seconds. "Didi," as he was known on the Riviera, could skin dive to 60 feet.

My friends harnessed the three-cylinder block on my back with the regulator riding at the nape of my neck and the hoses looped over my head. I spat on the inside of my shatterproof glass mask and rinsed it in the surf so that mist would not form inside. I molded the soft rubber flanges of the mask tightly over forehead and cheekbones. I fitted the mouthpiece under my lips and gripped the nodules between my teeth. A vent the size of a paper clip was to pass my inhalations and exhalations beneath the sea. Staggering under the 50-pound apparatus, I walked with a Charlie Chaplin waddle into the sea.

The diving lung was designed to be slightly buoyant. I reclined in the chilly water to estimate my compliance with Archimedes' principle that a solid body immersed in liquid is buoyed up by a force equal to the weight of the liquid displaced. Dumas justified me with Archimedes by attaching seven pounds of lead to my belt. I sank gently to the sand. I breathed sweet effortless air. There was a faint whistle when I inhaled and a light rippling sound of bubbles when I breathed out. The regulator was adjusting pressure precisely to my needs.

I looked into the sea with the same sense of trespass that I have felt on every dive. A modest canyon opened below, full of dark green weeds, black sea urchins and small flowerlike white algae. Fingerlings browsed in the scene. The sand sloped down into a clear blue infinity. The sun struck so brightly I had to squint. My arms hanging at my sides, I kicked the fins languidly and traveled down, gaining speed, watching the beach reeling past. I stopped kicking and the momentum carried me on a fabulous glide. When I stopped, I slowly emptied my lungs and held my breath. The diminished volume of my body decreased the lifting force of water, and I sank dreamily down. I inhaled a great chestful and retained it. I rose toward the surface.

My human lungs had a new role to play, that of a sensitive ballasting system. I took normal breaths in a slow rhythm, bowed my head and swam smoothly down to 30 feet. I felt no increasing water pressure, which at that depth is twice that of the surface. The aqualung automatically fed me increased compressed air to meet the new pressure layer. Through the fragile human lung linings this counter-pressure was being transmitted to the blood stream and instantly spread throughout the incompressible body. My brain received no subjective news of the pressure. I was at ease, except for a pain in the middle ear and sinus cavities. I swallowed as one does in a landing airplane to open my Eustachian tubes and healed the pain. (I did not wear ear plugs, a dangerous practice when under water. Ear plugs would have trapped a pocket of air between them and the eardrums. Pressure building up in the Eustachian tubes would have forced my eardrums outward, eventually to the bursting point.)

I reached the bottom in a state of transport. A school of silvery sars (goat bream), round and flat as saucers, swam in a rocky chaos. I looked up and saw the surface shining like a defective mirror. In the center of the looking glass was the trim silhouette of Simone, reduced to a doll. I waved. The doll waved at me.

I became fascinated with my exhalations. The bubbles swelled on the way up through lighter pressure layers, but were peculiarly flattened like mushroom caps by their eager push against the medium. I conceived the importance bubbles were to have for us in the dives to come. As long as air boiled on the surface all was well below. If the bubbles disappeared there would be anxiety, emergency measures, despair. They roared out of the regulator and kept me company. I felt less alone.

I swam across the rocks and compared myself favorably with the sars. To swim fishlike, horizontally, was the logical method in a medium eight hundred times denser than air. To halt and hang attached to nothing, no lines or air pipe to the surface, was a dream. At night I had often had visions of flying by extending my arms as wings. Now I flew without wings. (Since that first aqualung flight, I have never had a dream of flying.)

I thought of the helmet diver arriving where I was on his ponderous boots and struggling to walk a few yards, obsessed with his umbilici and his head imprisoned in copper. On skin dives I had seen him leaning dangerously forward to make a step, clamped in heavier pressure at the ankles than the head, a cripple in an alien land. From this day forward we would swim across miles of country no man had known, free and level, with our flesh feeling what the fish scales know.

I experimented with all possible maneuvers of the aqualung—loops, somersaults and barrel rolls. I stood upside down on one finger and burst out laughing, a shrill distorted laugh. Nothing I did altered the automatic rhythm of air. Delivered from gravity and buoyancy I flew around in space.

I could attain almost two knots' speed, without using my arms. I soared vertically and passed my own bubbles. I went down to 60 feet. We had been there many times without breathing aids, but we did not know what happened below that boundary. How far could we go with this strange device?

Fifteen minutes had passed since I left the little cove. The regulator lisped in a steady cadence in the 10-fathom layer and I could spend an hour there on my air supply. I determined to stay as long as I could stand the chill. Here were tantalizing crevices we had been obliged to pass fleetingly before. I swam inch-by-inch into a dark narrow tunnel, scraping my chest on the floor and ringing the air tanks on the ceiling. In such situations a man is of two minds. One urges him on toward mystery and the other reminds him that he is a creature with good sense that can keep him alive, if he will use it. I bounced against the ceiling. I'd used one-third of my air and was getting lighter. My brain complained that this foolishness might sever my air hoses. I turned over and hung on my back.

The roof of the cave was thronged with lobsters. They stood there like great flies on a ceiling. Their heads and antennae were pointed toward the cave entrance. I breathed lesser lungsful to keep my chest from touching them. Above water was occupied, ill-fed France. I thought of the hundreds of calories a diver loses in cold water. I selected a pair of one-pound lobsters and carefully plucked them from the roof, without touching their stinging spines. I carried them toward the surface.

Simone had been floating, watching my bubbles wherever I went. She swam down toward me. I handed her the lobsters and went down again as she surfaced. She came up under a rock which bore a torpid Provençal citizen with a fishing pole. He saw a blonde girl emerge from the combers with lobsters wriggling in her hands. She said, "Could you please watch these for me?" and put them on the rock. The fisherman dropped his pole.

Simone made five more surface dives to take lobsters from me and carry them to the rock. I surfaced in the cove, out of the fisherman's sight. Simone claimed her lobster swarm. She said, "Keep one for yourself, monsieur. They are very easy to catch if you do as I did."

Lunching on the treasures of the dive, Tailliez and Dumas questioned me on every detail. We reveled in plans for the aqualung. Tailliez penciled the tablecloth and announced that each yard of depth we claimed in the sea would open to mankind 300,000 cubic kilometers of living space. Tailliez, Dumas and I had come a long way together. We had been eight years in the sea as goggle divers. Our new key to the hidden world promised wonders. We recalled the beginning. . . .

Our first tool was the underwater goggle, a device that was known centuries ago in Polynesia and Japan, was used by sixteenth-century Mediterranean coral divers, and has been rediscovered about every decade in the last fifty years. The naked human eye, which is almost blind under water, can see clearly through watertight spectacles.

One Sunday morning in 1936 at Le Mourillon, near Toulon, I waded into the Mediterranean and looked into it through Fernez goggles. I was a regular Navy gunner, a good swimmer interested only in perfecting my crawl style. The sea was merely a salty obstacle that burned my eyes. I was astounded by what I saw in the shallow shingle at Le Mourillon, rocks covered with green, brown and silver forests of algae and fishes unknown to me, swimming in crystalline water. Standing up to breathe I saw a trolley car, people, electric-light poles. I put my eyes under again and civilization vanished with one last bow. I was in a jungle never seen by those who floated on the opaque roof.

Sometimes we are lucky enough to know that our lives have been changed, to discard the old, embrace the new, and run headlong down an immutable course. It happened to me at Le Mourillon on that summer's day, when my eyes were opened on the sea.

Soon I listened hungrily to gossip about heroes of the Mediterranean, with their Fernez goggles, Le Corlieu foot fins, and barbarous weapons to slay fish beneath the waves. At Sanary the incredible Le Moigne immersed himself in the ocean and killed fish with a slingshot!

There also was a fabulous creature named Frédéric Dumas, son of a physics professor, who speared fish with a curtain rod. These men were crossing the frontier of two hostile worlds.

Two years of goggle dives passed before I met Dumas. He told me how it had begun with him. "One day in the summer of 1938 I am out on the rocks when I see a real manfish, much further on in evolution than me. He never lifts his head to breathe, and after a surface dive water spouts out of a tube he has in his mouth. I am amazed to see rubber fins on his feet. I sit admiring his agility and wait until he gets cold and has to come in. His name is Lieutenant de Vaisseau Philippe Tailliez. His undersea gun works on the same theory as mine. Tailliez's goggles are bigger than mine. He tells me where to get goggles and fins and how to make a breathing pipe from a garden hose. We make a date for a hunting party. This day is a big episode in my undersea life."

The day was important for each of us. It brought Tailliez, Dumas and me into a diving team. I already knew Tailliez.

Undersea hunting raged, with arbalests, spears, spring guns, cartridge-propelled arrows, and the elegant technique of the American writer, Guy Gilpatric, who impaled fish with fencing lunges. The fad resulted in almost emptying the littoral of fish and arousing the commercial fishermen to bitter anger. They claimed we drove away fish, damaged nets, looted their seines, and caused mistrals with our schnorkels.

One day, however, when Dumas was diving he noticed a picturesque individual watching him from a large power boat, a formidable man stripped to the waist. He exhibited a gallery of torsoid tattoos consisting of dancing girls and famous generals such as Maréchal Lyautey and "Papa" Joffre. Didi winced as the individual hailed him, for he recognized Carbonne, the dreaded Marseilles gangster, whose idol was Al Capone.

Carbonne summoned Didi to his ladder and handed him aboard. He asked him what he was doing. "Oh, just diving," Didi said warily.

"I am always coming out here to take a peaceful rest from the city," said Carbonne. "I like what you are doing. I wish you to conduct all of your activities from my ship."

Didi's patron heard about the fishermen's hatred of divers. It incensed him and, cruising among the fishing boats with his hairy arm flung over Didi's shoulder, he bawled out, "Hey, you fellows—don't forget this is *my friend!*"

We twitted Didi about his gangster, but noted that the fishermen no longer molested him. They diverted their protests to the government, which passed a law severely regulating underwater hunting. Air-breathing apparatus and cartridge-propelled harpoons were forbidden. Divers were required to take out hunting licenses and join a recognized spear-fishing club. But from Menton to Marseilles the shore had emptied of larger fauna. Another remarkable thing was noticed. The big pelagic fish had learned how to stay out of range of weapons. They would insolently keep 5 feet away from a slingshot, exactly beyond its range. A rubber-propelled harpoon gun, which could shoot 8 feet, found the fish a little over 8 feet away. They stayed 15 feet from the biggest harpoon guns. For ages man had been the most harmless animal under water. When he suddenly learned underwater combat, the fish promptly adopted safety tactics.

In the goggle-diving era Dumas made a light-hearted bet at Le Brusq that he could spear 220 pounds of fish in two hours. He made five dives within the time limit, to depths of 45 to 60 feet. On each dive he speared and fought a mammoth fish in the short period he could hold his breath. He brought up four groupers and an 80-pound liche (palomata or leer-fish). Their total weight was 280 pounds.

One of our favorite memories is of a fighting liche which probably weighed 200 pounds. Didi speared him and we went down in relays to fight him. Twice we managed to drag him to the surface in our arms. The big fellow seemed to like air as much as we did. He gained strength as we wore out, and at last the monarch of liches escaped.

We were young and sometimes we went beyond the limits of common sense. Once Tailliez was diving alone in December at Carqueiranne, with his dog Soika guarding his clothes. The water was 52° Fahrenheit. Philippe was trying to spear some big sea bass but had to break off the chase when he could no longer stand the cold. He found himself several hundred yards from the deserted shore. The return swim was a harrowing, benumbed struggle. He dragged himself out on a rock and fainted. A bitter wind swept him. He had small chance of surviving such an exposure. The wolfhound, moved by an extraordinary instinct, covered him with its body and breathed hot air on his face. Tailliez awoke with near-paralyzed hands and feet and stumbled to a shelter.

Our first researches in diving physiology were attempts to learn about cold. Water is a better heat conductor than air and has an extreme capacity for draining off calories. Bodily heat lost in sea bathing is enormous, placing a grave strain on the central heating plant of the body. The body must above all keep its central temperature constant. Exposed to cold the body makes a ruthless strategic retreat, first abandoning the skin to cold and then the subcutaneous layer, by means of vaso-constriction of the superficial blood vessels—gooseflesh. If the cold continues to draw off heat, the body will surrender the hands and feet to conserve the vital center. When the inner temperature drops life is in danger.

We learned that bathers who wrapped in blankets were doing exactly the wrong thing. A covering does not restore heat, it merely requires the central heating plant to burn up more calories to flush warmth into the outer layer. The process is accompanied by severe nervous reactions. By the same token hot drinks and alcohol are useless in restoring surface temperature. We sometimes take a drink of brandy after a hard dive, rather for its depressant effect than with any expectation of gaining warmth from it. We learned that the best way to restore heat is the most obvious one, to get into a very hot bath or stand between two fires on the beach.

We discovered a surprising fact about the practice of coating oneself with grease for cold swims. Grease does not stick to the skin. It washes away, leaving a mere film of oil, which, far from protecting the swimmer, slightly increases the loss of caloric heat. Grease would be acceptable insulation, however, if it could be injected under the skin to simulate the splendid blubber underwear of the whale.

To protect myself from cold I spent days tailoring and vulcanizing rubberized garments. In the first one, I looked something like Don Quixote. I made another which could be slightly inflated to provide more insulation, but there was only one depth in which the suit was equilibrated, and I spent most of the time fighting against being hauled up or down. Another weakness of this dress was that the air would rush to the feet, leaving me in a stationary, head-down position. Finally, in 1946, we evolved the constant-volume dress we use now in cold water. It is inflated by the diver's nasal exhalations, blown out under the edges of an inner mask. Air escape valves at the head, wrist and ankles keep the diver stable in any depth or bodily position. Marcel Ichac, the explorer, found it effective in dives under Greenland ice floes on the Paul-Émile Victor Arctic expedition. Dumas has designed a "mid-season" dress, a featherlight foam rubber jerkin which protects for twenty minutes in cold water and leaves the diver all his agility.

Vanity colored our early skin dives. We plumed ourselves at the thought that we late-comers could attain the working depths of pearl and sponge divers who had made their first plunges as infants. In 1939 on Djerba Island, off Tunisia, I witnessed and confirmed with a sounding line a remarkable dive by a sixty-year-old Arab sponge diver. Without breathing apparatus he reached 130 feet, in an immersion time of two and one-half minutes.

The ordeals of such dives are only for the exceptional man. As the naked diver sounds through increasing pressure layers, the air in his lungs is physically shrunk. Human lungs are balloons in a flexible cage, which is literally squeezed in under pressure. At a hundred feet down the air in the balloon occupies one-fourth the space it does at the surface. Further down the ribs reach a position of inflexibility and may crack and collapse.

However, the working depth of sponge divers is usually not more than the three-atmosphere strata, 66 feet, where their rib cages are reduced to one-third normal size. We learned to go that deep without apparatus. We made 60-foot dives of two-minute durations, aided by several pounds of belt weights. Under 25 feet the weights became heavier in proportion to the compression of the rib cage, so that there was a certain uneasiness about meeting with accidents while weighted to the bottom.

Dumas's skin-diving technique consisted of floating face under water and breathing through a schnorkel tube. When he spotted some attraction below, he would execute a maneuver called the *coup de reins*, literally "stroke of the loins," the technique the whale uses to sound. For a floating man, it consists of bending from the waist and pointing the head and torso down. Then the legs are thrown up in the air with a powerful snap and the diver plummets straight down. Lightning dives require well-trained, wide-open Eustachian tubes to deal with the rapidly mounting pressure.

When we had attained the zone of sponge divers we had no particular sense of satisfaction, because the sea concealed enigmas that we could only glimpse in lightning dives. We wanted breathing equipment, not so much to go deeper, but to stay longer, simply to live a while in the new world. We tried Commandant Le Prieur's independent diving gear, a cylinder of compressed air slung across the chest and releasing a continuous flow into a face mask. The diver manually valved the air to meet pressure and cut down waste. We had our first grand moments of leisure in the sea with Le Prieur's lung. But the continuous discharge of air allowed only short submersions.

The gunsmith of my cruiser, the *Suffren,* built an oxygen rebreathing apparatus I designed. He transformed a gas-mask canister of soda lime, a small oxygen bottle, and a length of motorbike inner tube into a lung that repurified exhalations by filtering out the carbon dioxide in the soda lime. It was self-contained, one could swim with it, and it was silent. Swimming 25 feet down with the oxygen apparatus was the most serene thrill I have had in the water. Silent and alone in a trancelike land, one was accepted by the sea. My euphoria was all too short.

Having been told that oxygen was safe down to 45 feet, I asked two sailors from the *Suffren* to man a dinghy above me while I dived to the boundary of oxygen. I went down with a ceremonious illusion. I was accepted in the sea jungle and would pay it the compliment of putting aside my anthropoid ways, clamp my legs together and swim down with the spinal undulations of a porpoise. Tailliez had demonstrated that a man could swim on the surface without using arms or legs. I borrowed the characteristics of a fish, notwithstanding certain impediments such as my anatomy and a 10-pound lead pipe twisted around my belt.

I undulated through the amazingly clear water. Ninety feet away I saw an aristocratic group of silver and gold giltheads wearing their scarlet gill patches like British brigadiers. I wiggled toward them and got very close without alarming them. My fish personality was fairly successful, but I remembered that I could swim a great deal faster by crudely kicking my fins. I started chasing a fish and cornered him off in his cave. He bristled his dorsal fins and rolled his eyes uneasily. He made a brave decision and sprang at me, escaping by inches. Below I saw a big blue dentex (bream) with a bitter mouth and hostile eyes. He was hanging about 45 feet down. I descended and the fish backed away, keeping a good distance.

Then my lips began to tremble uncontrollably. My eyelids fluttered.

My spine was bent backward like a bow.

With a violent gesture I tore off the belt weight and lost consciousness.

The sailors saw my body reach the surface and quickly hauled me into the boat.

I had pains in neck and muscles for weeks. I thought my soda lime must have been impure. I spent the winter on the *Suffren* building an improved oxygen lung, one that would not induce convulsions. In the summer I went back to the same place off Porquerolles and went down 45 feet with the new lung. I convulsed so suddenly that I do not remember jettisoning my belt weight. I came very near drowning. It was the end of my interest in oxygen.

In the summer of 1939 I made a speech at a dinner party, explaining why war could not come for at least ten years. Four days later I was aboard my cruiser, speeding west under secret orders; the next day at Oran we heard the declaration of war. At our ship line lay a division of Royal Navy torpedo boats, one of which was disabled by a heavy steel cable fouled in her screw. There were no navy divers at Oran. I volunteered to make a skin dive to survey the situation.

Even the sight of the screw did not cool my ardor: the thick wire was wound six times around the shaft and several times around the blades. I called on five good skin divers from my ship, and we dived repeatedly to hack away the cable. After hours of work clearing the propeller, we crawled back on our ship, barely able to stand. The torpedo boat sailed out with its division, and as it passed, the crew turned out in a line at the rail and gave three cheers for the crazy Frenchmen. That day I learned that heavy exertion under water was madness. It was absolutely necessary to have breathing apparatus to do such jobs.

Later in the war while I was working for Naval Intelligence in Marseilles against the occupying powers, my commander insisted that I continue diving experiments when my duties permitted. Diving helped camouflage the secret work. I tested the Fernez diving apparatus, which consisted of an air pipe from a surface pump. The pipe was carried across the diver's face to a duck-beak valve which released a constant flow of pumped air. The diver tapped the flow with a mouthpiece, sucking the air he needed. It was the simplest diving gear ever designed. It tethered a man to the surface and unnecessarily wasted half the air, but at least it did not use treacherous oxygen.

I was enjoying the full breaths of the Fernez pump one day at 40 feet when I felt a strange shock in my lungs. The rumble of exhaust bubbles stopped. Instantly I closed my glottis, sealing the remaining air in my lungs. I hauled on the air pipe and it came down without resistance. The pipe had broken near the surface. I swam to the boat. Later I realized the danger I had faced. If I hadn't instinctively shut the air valve in my throat the broken pipe would have fed me thin surface air and the water would have collapsed my lungs in the frightful "squeeze."

In testing devices in which one's life is at stake, such accidents induce zeal for improvement. We were working on defenses against broken pipes one day with Dumas 75 feet down, breathing from the Fernez pipe. I was in the tender, watching the pipe, when I saw it rupture. Dumas was trapped in pressure three times greater than the surface. I grabbed the pipe before it sank and reeled it in frantically, ill with suspense. I could feel heavy tugs from below. Then Dumas appeared, red-faced and choking, his eyes bulging. But he was alive. He, too, had locked his glottis in time and had then climbed the pipe hand over hand. We worked on the gear until it operated more reliably, but the pump could take us no further. It fastened us on a leash and we wanted freedom.

We were dreaming about a self-contained compressed-air lung. Instead of Le Prieur's hand valve, I wanted an automatic device that would release air to the diver without his thinking about it, something like the demand system used in the oxygen masks of high-altitude fliers. I went to Paris to find an engineer who would know what I was talking about. I had the luck to meet Émile Gagnan, an expert on industrial-gas equipment for a huge international corporation. It was December, 1942, when I outlined my demands to Émile. He nodded encouragingly and interrupted. "Something like this?" he asked and handed me a small bakelite mechanism. "It is a demand valve I have been working on to feed cooking gas automatically into the motors of automobiles." At the time there was no petrol for automobiles and all sorts of projects were under way for utilizing the fumes of burning charcoal and natural gas. "The problem is somewhat the same as yours," said Émile.

In a few weeks we finished our first automatic regulator. Émile and I selected a lonely stretch of the river Marne for a test dive. He stood on the bank while I waded in over my head. The regulator furnished plenty of air without effort on my part. But the air rushed wastefully out of the exhaust pipe in the fashion of the Fernez gear. I tried standing on my head. The air supply almost ceased. I couldn't breathe. I tried swimming horizontally, and the air flowed in a perfectly controlled rhythm. But how were we going to dive if we couldn't operate vertically?

Chilled and disappointed, we drove home, analyzing the regulator's reason for such tricks. Here it was, a miracle of design, the first stage efficiently reducing one hundred and fifty atmospheres to six atmospheres, and the second control stage rationing that to breathing density and volume. Before we reached Paris we had the answer.

When I was standing up in the water the level of the exhaust was higher than the intake and that six-inch difference in pressure allowed the air to overflow. When I stood on my head, the exhaust was six inches lower, suppressing the air flow. When I swam horizontally, the exhaust and intake were in the same pressure level and the regulator worked perfectly. We arrived at the simple solution of placing the exhaust as close as possible to the intake so that pressure variations could not disrupt the flow. The improvement worked perfectly in a tank test in Paris.

The Bends

by

Captain Edward Ellsberg

We have mentioned the handicaps of the diving suit compared with the aqualung, but for prolonged immersion in limited areas, for example in rescue and salvage work, it continues to be extensively used. The diver may be connected with a surface craft by both rope and breathing tube, yet his occupation remains hazardous. Sometimes death strikes with horrifying suddenness. Sometimes permanent damage, such as lifelong paralysis, can result from some unforeseen happening. No one is more thoroughly acquainted with the problems than Captain Edward Ellsberg, author of the chapter that follows. A lifetime in the United States Navy qualified him as one of the world's greatest salvage experts. He won the Distinguished Service Medal for his work in raising the sunken submarine S-51. From Block Island to Normandy and North Africa, he served his country in two world wars. Here is the drama and the danger that attended one of his greatest exploits.

DIVING is queer business. Dangerous? Yes. But not for the weird reasons that lurid fiction writers and melodramatic authors, who usually know no more of diving than they do of conditions on Mars, have fed their readers.

What makes diving difficult and dangerous? To the diver the world over, whether Greek, Kanaka, Japanese, Italian, or American, who is diving to accomplish a specific commercial result and not merely to provide faked movie thrills or melodramatic books, it's neither the devilfish nor the shark that must be battled hand to hand in desperate combat on the sea floor. It isn't the villainous conspirator bent on severing a diver's air hose and robbing him of the treasure he has salvaged from the deep—those chests of gold and bushels of pearls and rubies which the public has been led to believe always pave the bottom of the sea. It is none of these fantastic imaginings. What the difficulty actually is—what the danger always has been from the days, thousands of years ago, when the first savage, plunging beneath the surface, sought to bring up sponge or pearl from the depths—is the very prosaic fact that water has weight, plenty of it.

As nature made both us and this world in which we

exist, we live and have our being at the bottom of an ocean of air—a very deep ocean, extending scores and scores of miles above us, but with the air rapidly thinning away toward a vacuum only a few miles up. The cumulative weight of this gaseous ocean presses down on us, enters our lungs, permeates our bodies; and nature has through countless eons evolved our organisms to stand this pressure which, registered on the ordinary barometer, averages about 14.7 pounds to the square inch. This we call a pressure of one atmosphere. Our brains, our nerves, our lungs, our entire bodies are accustomed to function under this atmospheric pressure; if it be varied much, either up or down, discomfort and even distress promptly follow.

It is a widely observed fact that people with weak hearts find it dangerous to cross high mountains, to live in high altitudes, or to travel very high in [unpressurized] airplanes. The reason, of course, is that as such individuals go up and the air pressure decreases they commence to pant violently, trying to get enough of the rarer air into their lungs to give their bodies the oxygen they need. Their weak hearts sometimes give way under the added strain.

Yet even under these circumstances, the change of pressure and variation in the amount of air inspired per breath are relatively insignificant compared with the changes which a deep sea diver has to bear. For instance, atop Pike's Peak, some 14,100 feet above sea level, which is as high as most people are ever likely to get, the pressure drops about four tenths of an atmosphere—from 14.7 pounds per square inch (which is the sea level average) to around 8.7 pounds, decreasing some 6 pounds. This decrease of about 40 per cent from normal in pressure causes many people acute distress and makes even the average person pant violently in climbing the few steps to the observatory tower, so closely has nature tuned us to what she considers normal and so little are we able to bear deviations from that normal.

Consider now the diver. Sea water is heavy; a cubic foot of it weighs 64 pounds. For every foot below the surface the diver goes he has added to the weight of the sea pressing on each square foot of his body a further load of 64 pounds; or .445 pounds on every square inch of his body. He need descend but 14 feet below the surface of the sea to raise the pressure on his body by the same amount, 6 pounds, that an ascent of 14,100 feet to the top of Pike's Peak decreases it. And he need go but 33 feet below the surface of the sea to double the pressure on him—to make it twice what nature intended him to bear.

Now 33 feet is no great depth for a diver who must take wrecks where he finds them; working depths beyond 100 feet are not uncommon. What does that mean to the diver?

On the *S-51*, we worked for months at 132 feet, 22 fathoms down. At that depth, the water pressure on the sea floor was 4¼ tons to the square foot, or 59 pounds to the square inch, and the diver had a total load bearing on every square inch of him of five atmospheres, just five times what nature had designed him to stand! Over the entire surface of his body lay a pressure of nearly 60 tons, a load easily capable of reducing him to jelly (and which to some unfortunate divers has done just that).

Owing then to the extreme weight of water, it is obvious that a deep sea diver faces extraordinary conditions and dangers under which he must live and work. Compared to these perilous conditions, the tinsel devilfish and sharks with which the literature of diving is festooned fade into insignificance.

What results? To live and work under water for more than a few scant minutes, it is of course obvious that a diver must continuously be supplied with air. To prevent his chest from being crushed in by the terrific load on it in deep water, this air must be supplied him at a pressure slightly greater than that of the water surrounding him. And mechanically to permit him to breathe at all, there must be some device, over his head at least, to keep the water away from his nostrils while he breathes.

Centuries of slow development evolved at last, in the hands of Siebe, Gorman and Company of London, the present combination of a rigid copper helmet bolted tightly to a watertight canvas and rubber suit, properly weighted, as best fulfilling the mechanical necessities of a diving rig. Air is fed into the helmet in a steady stream and, after it has been breathed, escapes to the sea through a spring-loaded exhaust valve. The air breathed into the lungs, at a pressure slightly above that of the sea bottom, communicates its pressure through the blood to every part of the diver's body, putting him under an internal pressure counterbalancing that of the sea pressing on him externally. In this condition of equilibrium, the diver can stand any depth of sea without being crushed.

Normally, then, the diver is in balance between two opposing forces of great magnitude, and his state may fairly well be illustrated by comparison with that of a pneumatic tire on a heavily loaded truck. So long as the tire is inflated with sufficient compressed air, it stays rounded out and supports the load pressing down upon it. But if the tire "blows out," down comes the weight of the truck upon it and flattens it to a pancake. In the same way, if the diver by any chance loses the air pressure in his suit, down comes the weight of the sea upon him and instantly crushes him as flat as any blown-out tire.

To live, then, beneath the sea, the diver in the usual helmet and flexible suit must breathe compressed air, under pressures of three, four, five, or even more atmospheres, pressures far above that existing on the surface, to which nature has accustomed us; and the results of breathing under such unnatural conditions lead directly to the gravest danger that a diver faces, that of "the bends."

Not many decades ago, when diving was relatively in its infancy, though the diving rig used had been fairly well developed to its present state, divers began to notice that, if they went much below depths of 60 feet or stayed down very long at that depth, say much over an hour, when they came back to the surface they were shortly attacked by a mysterious disease, causing intense pain and doubling the victim up in strange contortions. From the convulsive movements of the sufferers the malady received the slang name "the bends." For those unfortunates who had gone much below 60 feet or had worked there several hours, "the bends" often took a more serious form; paralysis set in, making the victim a helpless cripple for life, and in some cases, even, quick death ensued, coming within a short time after emerging from the water.

What caused these afflictions the divers could never figure out. It was simply obvious that strange death and quick disaster lurked in the ocean depths for such as dared penetrate them, usually in search of sunken treasure. What is unaccountable is naturally doubly terrifying, and to the men involved it seemed that malignant demons lurked on the ocean floor, intent on punishing the plunderers who sought to rob the wrecks the sea had once claimed for its own. Still the lure of sunken gold is strong; some men escaped attack, and, in spite of sudden death and of even more horrible complete paralysis, deep diving continued spasmodically, with the victims of "the bends" fatalistically accepting their curse.

Had it been left to divers only to solve the mystery, it is probable that the matter would still be in the realm of superstition, but the advancing needs of engineering brought the problem forcibly to the attention of scientists. The construction of tunnels under rivers (developed in the nineteenth century) and the necessity of providing deep foundations along river banks for huge bridges brought in as an indispensable tool the caisson. This, maintained under moderate air pressure, kept back the water while the laborers, euphemistically called "sandhogs," burrowed through the water-soaked muck and clay to advance their bore or sink their footings. Here again were soon noted the symptoms of the dreaded diver's malady; but now, with hundreds of men involved, the fatalities jumped, the number of cases of "the bends" multiplied, and the work suffered.

But "the bends" did not confine itself to the sandhogs. It struck at a more notable victim. The Brooklyn Bridge, with by far the longest span of its time, required extraordinary caisson work for its pier foundations in the soft mud beneath the level of the East River. Its builder, Washington Augustus Roebling, spent so much time personally supervising the caisson work on the success of which his mighty bridge structure depended that he shortly was struck down himself by the compressed air illness, and for ten years, from 1873 to the completion of the bridge in 1883, was compelled to direct the construction from his sick bed.

"The bends" began to receive scientific attention for the first time. Under the more dignified title of "caisson disease," science turned an inquiring eye on the problem, and very quickly dissipated the mists of superstition. In 1860, as a preliminary, came the first inkling, when a Frenchman, Professor Leroy de Mericourt, expounded the theory that the diver's blood becomes surcharged with the air which he breathes under heavy pressure; but it was left to his compatriot, Monsieur Paul Bert, in 1878, after Roebling's disaster, first to investigate the disease seriously, to expound the causes of "the bends," and to indicate the first crude method of avoidance.

Bert demonstrated that the disease was due wholly to bubbles of a gas, nitrogen, which appeared in the blood and tissues of a diver on emerging from the surface. Professor de Mericourt had demonstrated how the gas came on the scene. Briefly the situation is explainable about as follows:

The air we breathe is composed roughly of 21 per cent of oxygen (the essential gas for sustaining life), and 78 per cent of nitrogen (a wholly inert gas which simply dilutes the oxygen), with the remaining 1 per cent a mixture of carbon dioxide and certain other rare gases which may here be neglected. As we breathe under ordinary conditions, this mixture of gases is inhaled into the lungs, where, over the extended surfaces and cells of those organs, it comes into intimate contact with the blood. The result is that part of the oxygen is converted into carbon dioxide and the remainder—together with the nitrogen, the newly formed carbon dioxide, and some additional moisture —is expelled on exhalation.

But the diver's conditions of breathing are far from

ordinary. If he is breathing air under a pressure of five atmospheres, a strange thing happens with each breath. So great is the pressure now in his lungs that the nitrogen, instead of passing harmlessly out, is forced to dissolve in the blood. With each repeated breath more nitrogen is dissolved by the blood stream it meets in the lungs, to be carried thence to every part of the body where, under the same superpressure, it is taken up by the tissues, the fats, and the muscles.

The speed with which this absorption of nitrogen goes on is proportional to the pressure under which the diver is working, and its extent depends on the length of time he remains under that pressure. Consequently, deeper water means faster absorption and a longer stay means more gas dissolved, the total amount absorbed being a combination of both factors —depth and time.

Now while the diver is on the bottom, he never feels this process going on and is usually quite ignorant of it. But when he starts to ascend, trouble starts. In the old days it culminated in "the bends." As the diver rises, the sea pressure decreases; when he reaches the surface, it vanishes altogether. But it was this excess pressure which originally forced nitrogen to dissolve in his body, and only under that pressure will the nitrogen stay dissolved there. When the pressure decreases, the nitrogen, no longer able to stay in solution, starts to appear in the blood and elsewhere in the form of bubbles. As the pressure decreases further, more nitrogen comes out of solution, and meanwhile the original bubbles expand. The diver's blood stream, instead of being a liquid, commences to become a froth.

This condition can be best illustrated by a familiar example (an example first suggested by de Mericourt). Consider a bottle of some charged water, such as ginger ale, with the original cap intact and the bottle sealed. Held up to the light, the liquid in the bottle appears as a clear, solid fluid. That liquid contains, however, a considerable amount of a gas (in this case carbon dioxide) dissolved in it under several atmospheres of pressure; but, being in solution, the gas is invisible. Pull the cap and watch what happens.

Immediately the cap is removed, the pressure on the ginger ale is removed and drops to atmospheric. With the removal of that excess pressure, the gas begins to come out of solution, the liquid is permeated with visible bubbles, and (especially if the bottle is not chilled) the ginger ale foams up and overflows the neck of the bottle in a violent froth of escaping bubbles. Even for a considerable period after the cap is pulled, gas will continue to be liberated from solution, rising in a steady stream of bubbles toward the surface.

What happens to the uncapped bottle of ginger ale happens to the unfortunate diver who rises too rapidly to the surface after a long, deep dive. But in the case of the diver, the results are far more serious. If enough nitrogen has been absorbed in his system, bubbles large enough to clog his veins and block off circulation form here or there, causing the intense pain and convulsions of "the bends." In some cases, enough bubbles are carried to the heart to fill one side of it with accumulations of gas which stop its pumping action, causing quick death. In other cases (and relatively frequent ones in the old days) the bubbles lodge in the spinal column, causing paralysis (usually of the legs). The favorite lodging spot of bubbles in minor cases is in the joints, such as the knees, the elbows, and the fingers, causing marked pain but no fatalities.

The discovery of the cause of caisson disease indicated the remedy for it. Monsieur Bert deduced from his experiments and discoveries that if, instead of coming immediately to the surface after a dive, thus quickly losing all the pressure on his body, the diver were to rise slowly but steadily to the surface, the nitrogen dissolved in his body would slowly come out of solution as the pressure decreased, in quantities not sufficient at any time to cause sizable bubbles, and escape continuously through the lungs—a process which was called "decompression."

Until 1907, Bert's method of slow uniform decompression was generally used by divers and caisson workers, very considerably reducing the number of cases of "the bends" but unfortunately not completely eliminating them. On tunnel work in New York around the turn of this century there were still numerous cases of sandhogs, hours after they had received their usual decompression and left the job, collapsing on the streets. Ordinarily they were considered by passers-by and even police as simply sodden drunks and left in the gutters or carted unconscious to a police station to sleep off a supposed jag, which naturally they never did. After some sad experiences with cases of "the bends" thus handled, caisson workers were by law required always to wear a metal tag, warning observers that, in case of collapse anywhere, the wearer was to be rushed immediately to a specified hospital equipped to treat "the bends."

Obviously, Bert's decompression methods left much to be desired. In 1906, the British Admiralty undertook a further study of the subject, mainly carried out by Professor J. S. Haldane, a physiologist, together with the then Lieutenant G. C. C. Damant of the Royal Navy. Haldane discovered that Bert's uniform slow decompression did not positively insure desaturation of the blood and tissues. Paradoxically, Haldane's experiments showed it was much safer to decompress in stages—that is, to come up sharply part way, so as to cut the pressure on the diver in half. This sudden decrease would allow a considerable amount of nitrogen to emerge and escape, but under a residual pressure still large enough to prevent the formation of any bubbles of troublesome size. After a specified time at the first stage, the diver was to be raised sharply to the next stage, again halving the pressure on him, and here letting him stop a further period in the water for more nitrogen elimination. And so on to the surface, the idea being that each sharp decrease in pressure would bring about definite elimination, but that no one drop in pressure should be great enough to allow large bubbles to form.

Haldane's theories were correct. He worked out permissible lengths of dives to various depths, and decompression tables showing the stopping points and times of stop at each point for safe decompression. Since Haldane's day, careful observation of his decompression tables (slightly modified by later experimental work) has usually avoided attacks of "the bends." But the major drawback resulting from his work was his conclusion that, for safe decompression, the time a diver could spend on the bottom without soaking up too much nitrogen was decidedly limited.

The one weak point in Haldane's stage decompression is that it must of necessity fit the normal man decompressing under average physiological conditions. Unfortunately some divers, regardless of how carefully selected, vary from the normal, and even a normal individual has his days when his bodily reactions are far from normal. Heaven only knows what may happen then.

For instance, take the case that occurred while we were salvaging the *S-51*, 22 fathoms down, on the sea floor some 14 miles to the eastward of Block Island. It was mid-November, winter was approaching, the water was very cold. Of ten divers with whom we had started, about six were knocked out by general exhaustion and a succession of minor cases of "the bends." If work was to continue, some fresh divers would have to be employed.

Among the seamen acting as tenders was a petty officer, L'Heureux. He had done considerable diving in shallow water in previous years, and only the year before, in examining another wreck, had made at least one dive to a depth of about 190 feet. L'Heureux volunteered to dive on the *S-51*, and, as a decidedly promising candidate, was accepted.

Not to make things too difficult for his initial dive, it was decided to send him down first simply as a helper to another diver, Joe Eiben, who was thoroughly acquainted with the wreck. L'Heureux's task was to be only to hold a submarine lamp to light up the black interior of the *S-51*'s engine room, the while his mate did the actual work of closing some valves.

Joe Eiben was dressed first, hoisted over the side and disappeared down the descending line. L'Heureux's helmet was screwed on, he was lifted overboard, dropped into the sea, given the lamp, a powerful 1,000-watt submarine searchlight, and in his turn slid down the descending line (which was tied to the submarine's gun just forward of the conning tower). In a little over a minute after leaving the surface, L'Heureux's telephone tender announced:

"L'Heureux reports, 'On the bottom!' " So far, so good. L'Heureux's tender started to pay out his lifelines, to give him slack enough to go aft astern of the conning tower and follow Eiben down into the *S-51*'s machinery hatch.

A few minutes later, a third diver, Tom Eadie, was dressed and dropped overboard. His task was to work by himself on an independent job on the deck of the submarine forward.

Ten minutes went by. Below in our hull, anxiously watched by the engineers, compressors were throbbing, shaking the *Falcon* rhythmically with their pulsations as they hammered the air down through the sea to our three divers. At the rail, three tenders periodically "fished" the diver's air hoses to keep out a proper amount of slack. In the *Falcon*'s superstructure perched three other tenders, headsets strapped over their ears, transmitters in their hands, listening intently for any message from their divers below. Around us rolled the open sea, a moderate chop beating against the sides of the *Falcon*, while from her, radiating in all directions like the spokes of a huge wheel from the hub, ran out six heavy manila hawsers, shackled to buoys in a wide ring surrounding us to hold us steady over the wreck regardless of how wind and sea might shift.

The calm on the *Falcon*'s deck was broken by a call from her superstructure.

"Joe Eiben's just phoned! He wants to know when L'Heureux's coming down with that light! He says it's pitch black inside the engine room where he is and until he gets a light he can't do a damned thing!"

Puzzled, I looked up at the telephone tenders. L'Heureux, of course, was on the bottom and had already had far more than enough time to get aft to his job. Signaling the tender on L'Heureux's phone, I ordered briefly:

"Tell L'Heureux to quit wasting time and get aft with Joe!"

"Aye, aye, sir!" The tender bent over his transmitter, sang out the message to L'Heureux below, then repeated it, but in another moment reported:

"Sorry, sir, but L'Heureux don't answer!"

"Give me that telephone!" I reached up, caught the headset and transmitter dropped to me from the boat-skids above, swiftly slipped the receivers over my own ears and sang out:

"Hello, L'Heureux!"

No answer, unless what sounded like a somewhat explosive "Ha!" could be taken as one. Again and again I tried, but to each call, each question about where he was, why he didn't get aft, I got nothing more than that occasional "Ha!" exploding in my ears. I was getting nowhere, time was flying, the precious minutes in which Eiben should be working were being wasted while he waited in the black engine room for his light.

In disgust I sang out to the tender on Eiben's telephone set:

"Tell Joe to come up out of the engine room, go forward to the gun, get L'Heureux, and lead him back!" Then remembering that I had still a third man on the bottom, Tom Eadie, who had gone down after L'Heureux, I seized Eadie's telephone, asked him:

"Say, Tom, did you see anything of L'Heureux when you went down?"

Promptly came a reply from Eadie:

"Yeah! When I hit the sub, there was L'Heureux standing by the gun, not moving, an' holding up that light in the water like he was the Statue o' Liberty!" Eadie paused a moment to catch up on his breathing, then continued: "Knowing it was L'Heureux's first dip, I clapped him on the back, laid my own helmet against his, an' asked him was he all right. I thought L'Heureux answered 'Yeh' so I left him an' went forward on my own job!"

So the pressure had apparently frozen L'Heureux into immobility or he had completely lost his sense of direction in the dim depths, and was afraid to move. Still there was the possibility that he had started, but had wandered forward instead of aft. I sang out into Eadie's phone again:

"Tom, go aft from where you're working till you find L'Heureux!"

Anxiously I waited, cursing inwardly. I now had Eiben coming forward, Eadie going aft, along the submarine, both wasting their dives. But I instantly forgot all that when Eadie reported:

"On deck! He's not by the gun! I just bumped into Joe here and he says L'Heureux isn't anywhere aft either!"

Startled, I pondered that incredulously. My two divers had met amidships, one from forward, one from aft, and no L'Heureux between them. While it seemed impossible on the narrow deck of that submarine, still they must have missed him. But on the other hand, both were exceptionally good men, and that was highly unlikely. What then had happened to L'Heureux? With a sinking feeling in the stomach, I tried once more to raise L'Heureux on his own telephone. No answer.

And then from the depths came another message, excitedly ringing in my ears from Eadie's phone:

"On deck! I think I see a light out on the bottom, about a hundred feet off the sub's starboard beam, and it's going farther away all the time!"

"That must be L'Heureux, Tom! He must have fallen off the sub and he's lost! Slide down the side and chase him!"

Eiben lowered Eadie down the submarine's side, hand over hand paying out his lines till Eadie struck bottom. Then Eadie started out across the firm sands of the ocean floor, breasting his way through the water following that will-o'-the-wisp of a glimmer vaguely seen through the translucent depths. Finally he caught up with it. There was L'Heureux, aimlessly wandering over the sands, the brilliant light clasped in his hand still flashing hither and yon seeking for the submarine, while curious fish swam all about him, darting suddenly in and out of the searchlight's gleam.

Eadie took his shipmate by the hand and guided him back to the submarine, where Eiben hauled both of them up on deck. Practically all of their allotted hour on the bottom was gone; we signaled all three men to stand by to rise. Nevertheless, on the topside I heaved a deep sigh of relief, thankful that nothing worse than two completely wasted dives had resulted.

We started up the three men for decompression. Diving was over for the day; we had no more divers to send down. As the late afternoon waned, step by step we heaved the divers up through the cold sea, carefully decompressing them, giving even a little extra time at each stop for L'Heureux's benefit, to insure thoroughly decompressing him. Finally, as darkness fell, with over two hours having elapsed since their rise started, we hoisted the three dripping divers in over the *Falcon*'s side and dropped them on deck. The tenders rushed in to strip off their burdensome rigs.

I loitered near L'Heureux, curious to note whether he looked frightened after his queer mishap. Off came his helmet. I asked him how he felt.

"Fine, Mr. Ellsberg! Fine!"

No question about it; he wasn't bluffing. L'Heureux was positively bubbling over with mirth, as happy as if he had just come from a very live party. Unquestionably he had on what we called an "oxygen jag," a state of mild intoxication, similar to the alcoholic variety, induced occasionally in some divers by the exhilaration of the excessive oxygen breathed in heavily compressed air. It meant nothing and would soon pass off, but it did explain his queer silence and his otherwise inexcusable falling off the sub. The moment he had let go of the gun he had apparently staggered drunkenly overboard and as drunkenly had zigzagged away across the ocean.

Surgeon Flotte, our medical officer, and an outstanding authority on the physiology of diving, tall and lean, even muffled in his overcoat, came up, observed L'Heureux a moment, then confirmed my surmise.

"Oxygen intoxication," he muttered.

There was no gain in questioning L'Heureux. The cause of his mishap was evident. And there was even less profit in laying him out for having ruined our day's work, expensive as that loss was—it simply wasn't his fault if excessive oxygen had jazzed him up. Not to make him feel bad by questioning him further, I left.

The tenders finished undressing the divers, leaving the *Falcon*'s fantail a mess of wet lead shoes, lead belts, helmets, hoses, and sodden diving rigs, and the three, still in their underwear, hurried below for supper, already somewhat late.

Five minutes later, seated on a bench before the heavily laden mess table, L'Heureux, still as merry as ever, suddenly collapsed, pitched forward on the table, unconscious!

No need to ask questions in that company. "The bends" and a bad case of it! No one wasted time in futile first aid measures. Hastily his shipmates seized the silent figure of L'Heureux, unceremoniously rushed him up the steep ladder to the deck above, while a cry rang out forward:

"Dr. Flotte! Dr. Flotte!"

In through the round steel door of the recompression tank went L'Heureux's inert form, one diver dragging his head, another pushing on his legs. Running from the wardroom came Surgeon Flotte, to dive through the opening almost on L'Heureux's heels. The door clanged shut behind him. On went the compressed air, hissing gently into the chamber as was customary. Hastily Surgeon Flotte felt L'Heureux. No sign of heartbeat. The man was completely out, might die at any moment, might perhaps already be dead from bubbles of air clogging his heart. It was no time for routine measures. At any cost those bubbles must be reduced to a size small enough to pass through the heart valves, to allow circulation to continue. And only high air pressure could compress them enough for that.

Dr. Flotte sprang for the air valve and twisted it wide open. Immediately the low hiss of the incoming air changed to a loud roar and, under the terrific pressure of the high pressure air banks, air started to pour into that recompression chamber. The needle on the caisson gauge jumped like a race horse getting away from the barrier, continued rapidly round the dial. Twenty pounds—40—50. Dr. Flotte's ears began to ring. That was as high in pressure as we had ever gone before on anybody. But no stop now. Sixty pounds. Blood oozed in Flotte's nose and mouth, but still he kept the roaring in full blast. He must get the pressure up on L'Heureux, never mind himself. Seventy pounds, with the valve wide open, the needle still racing up the dial. Eighty pounds, a higher pressure by far than anybody on that diving job had ever before been subjected to, either on the bottom or in the tank, and, worst of all for Flotte, taken in one swift rush!

Eighty pounds was enough. Flotte shut off the air. Dizzy from the sudden impact of high pressure, ears ringing excruciatingly, he bent over L'Heureux, tore off his shirt. The diver's chest was covered with purple splotches, the result of the bursting of a myriad small blood vessels from expanding air. But that was a minor result of "the bends." The major question was circulation. Had he got those heart bubbles down before L'Heureux's heart had stopped forever?

Flotte bent over his chest, listened, then smiled wanly. His heroic treatment had succeeded. A faint heartbeat became perceptible, L'Heureux began to breathe again. The bubbles, compressed to one-sixth their previous size by the sudden application of pressure, were passing out of the heart; blood was beginning to pump through it once more.

Gradually then Flotte began to release the air from the chamber, decompressing L'Heureux by regular stages. But in spite of working over him all night through, in spite of everything that his medical skill could suggest, Flotte was never able to bring L'Heureux back to consciousness. Through the long hours he lay there as the air pressure went down, limp, unconscious, apparently paralyzed in some degree, simply breathing feebly.

At 3 A.M. Dr. Flotte emerged from the recompression chamber, weak and dazed from his own exertions and the shock of high pressure. He sought out Lieutenant Hartley, skipper of the *Falcon.*

"Everything that pressure can do for L'Heureux's been done. Everything that I can do for him here has been done. He's paralyzed and he's nearly gone. If we're going to save L'Heureux's life, we've got to get him to a hospital right away!"

The *Falcon* was 25 miles at sea from Newport and the nearest hospital, swinging to her six hawsers mooring us over the grave of the *S-51*. Getting out in a small boat to unshackle those six hawsers from the mooring buoys often took an hour. Hartley called me.

"We're getting under way for Newport at once with L'Heureux. No time to unmoor now. I'm going to cut the hawsers. O.K.?"

I nodded.

In a moment, from bow to stern, axes were flashing downward into the eight-inch manila hawsers that held us to our buoys, and the frayed ends of the hacked-off cables went flying overboard, the severed mooring lines drifting off in the waves like undulating sea serpents. Below, our forced draft fans commenced to shriek, pouring air into the furnaces as the oil burners, suddenly opened wide, began to spray huge quantities of fuel into the fires.

Quivering from keel to superstructure from racing engine and twirling propeller, we got under way in the darkness and headed under full power for Newport, radioing to the Naval Hospital there to have an ambulance waiting on the dock when we arrived.

At 7 A.M. in the early dawn, we transferred the still unconscious L'Heureux to the ambulance and sadly headed back to sea to pick up our severed hawsers.

That was mid-November. When we landed him, L'Heureux had been a man of something over 160 pounds weight. Within a few weeks, partial paralysis, including his kidneys, resulting from "the bends," had wasted him away to a skeleton of 70 pounds, and there for months he hovered precariously between life and death. Not until late the following July, after an eight-month struggle in the hospital, did he finally recover sufficiently to be discharged.

What happened to L'Heureux? Why didn't the decompression we gave him, when he rose from that unlucky dive, free him of nitrogen in the normal manner, save him from a disastrous case of "the bends"? We never knew; Dr. Flotte could never explain it. The man had once made a deeper dive than that and had come up unaffected. What was different on this occasion? We could only theorize. Something, a sort of mental shell shock so to speak, at finding himself on that smashed submarine, still the coffin of most of her crew, may have so upset his normal nervous and physical reactions that his blood circulation may have been much reduced during his rise, with the result that he failed to decompress properly and came up with abnormal quantities of nitrogen still in his blood, which very promptly, once he was no longer under pressure, came out of solution and knocked him cold.

That, at any rate, is all we know. Haldane's decompression tables are correct, and we as divers follow them to avoid the dreaded scourge of diving. But once in a while in the abnormal case they fail to work, and "the bends" are with us again, as frightening as ever.

An Effort of Genius

by
Wilbur Cross

The diving suit and aqualung offer one method of "going down." There is a completely different technique: using a rigid shell that encases the diver in a sort of little room. The first such device was the diving bell. It was open at the bottom but air pressure prevented the water from rising in it. The legendary Alexander the Great is said to have used such a bell in the fourth century B.C. *From this tiny shell have developed the bathysphere in which Dr. William Beebe went half a mile down, the bathyscaphe in which Jacques Piccard plunged to the bottom of the Challenger Deep, and, most important, the modern submarine.*

The submarine's history is long. Leonardo da Vinci suggested a diving boat but gave no details because he felt it too horrible an invention to develop. (Leo-

nardo did make sketches of a number of diving suits, including one with sandbags to hasten the descent, a face mask, and an air reservoir.) In 1620 Cornelius van Drebel, a Dutchman in the service of England, is said to have built a submarine which navigated under the Thames propelled by twelve rowers. The first submarine actually used to attack an enemy was constructed by an American, David Bushnell, in the Revolutionary War. The fascinating episode in which Bushnell, even though unsuccessful, showed how submarines could be used in naval warfare is described in the following chapter.

THE WATERS of the bay were dark except where patches of misty moonlight flickered across the rippled surface, and the sky had just enough gray along the horizon so that the black silhouettes of ships stood etched against it. Conditions were ideal for undersea attack. One vessel riding at anchor loomed darker and more commanding than the others—the enemy flagship—and it was toward this that a midget American submarine stealthily made her way. If she could navigate the reaches of the open bay without detection, her objective would be to unleash her warhead, with enough explosive to blast the largest warship from the water, at the chosen target.

Though the basic problems of undersea warfare were the same, this event did not take place during World War II, or World War I, or even within the life span of any living person. This was the first wartime submarine attack in history, a naval engagement that took place during the American Revolution late in the evening of September 6, 1776. And despite the fact that this episode was one of the most incredible in the history of American warfare, it has long been bypassed and forgotten, a story that sounds too exaggerated to be fiction and too unbelievable to be fact.

The roots of the story go far from any battlefront, to Yale College in 1775, where one David Bushnell was experimenting with the unlikely academic project of exploding gunpowder under water. The experiments seemed even more incongruous to those who knew the thirty-five-year-old Bushnell as a frail, scholarly man who had matriculated rather late after many years as a farmer in Saybrook, Connecticut.

"I pray we are not close by when David blows himself up" was the somewhat derisive comment of most of his classmates, who were far more inspired by romantic ideas of running off to join the Continental Army than by thoughts of scholarly pursuits.

Bushnell was obviously not Army material in the eyes of his friends. He seemed disinclined to join the troops as some of his classmates were doing and to all outward appearances was content to carry on his gunpowder experiments in comparative solitude. But inwardly Bushnell was an ardent patriot whose hope was to turn his inventive talents to some use that would throw consternation into the British ranks. Once he had devised an effective way of detonating gunpowder under water he concentrated on how to transport explosives to the point where they would do the most good for the cause of the Colonies.

The result was an ingenious invention, referred to by some as a "contraption" but by history as the first true submarine, named the *Turtle*. She was designed and built to carry a lone operator and a charge of gunpowder under water to a target. Unlike many later one-man submarines she was not designed as a suicide craft but a vessel of war that could be used again and again in combat with the enemy. In the fall of 1775, after a great deal of secrecy to keep the strange craft's existence from the ears of British sympathizers, Bushnell carted the *Turtle* to the banks of the Connecticut River near Lyme. The big question was, Would she float? And if she floated, would she then be maneuverable?

The shape of the *Turtle* was halfway between that of an egg and a clam standing on end. She was built of warped oak planking, much like barrel staves, caulked and tarred at the joints, and reinforced with iron bands. In outside dimensions, she was 7 feet high, 4 feet long and 3 feet at the thickest width, with a keel consisting of 700 pounds of lead, 200 pounds of which could be jettisoned from inside the craft in the event of accident or leaking. At her stern was a small rudder, operable by a lever inside which ran through a crude stuffing box. Above the rudder perched a large box, concave on one side to fit the rounded hull, in which was stored 130 pounds of gunpowder. This was held in place by a locking device that could be tripped from inside and was attached by a short piece of line to a curious foot-long iron screw that projected above the craft. The screw could be turned with a crank inside so that, acting like an auger bit, it would bore upward into the wooden hull of a ship. Bushnell's ingenuity had so contrived this device that the bit could then be disengaged and left sticking in the hull, trailing the gunpowder container at the end of the line, while the *Turtle* escaped from the scene.

The torpedo, as the container of explosive was loosely called, had enough buoyancy so that it would barely break the surface of the water if permitted to drift free. This arrangement was carefully planned, not only so that its weight would not pull the screw loose from the ship's bottom, but so that its release from the *Turtle* would not alter the submarine's buoyancy by more than a few pounds. The locking device was attached, as a safety lever, to the clockwork of the torpedo so that the timer would not start clicking off

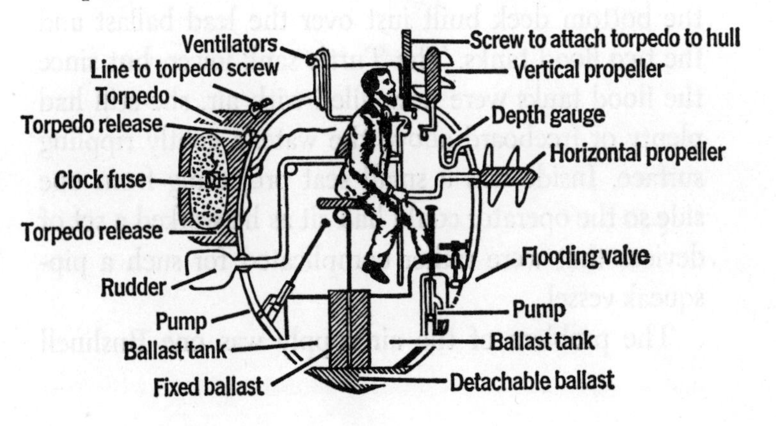

the thirty-minute predetonation interval until the submarine had separated itself from its lethal cargo.

The submarine was topped by a crude prototype of the conning tower, a molded bowl of brass 20 inches long, 7 inches high and shaped roughly like a derby hat. This was hinged at one end so that the operator could enter, had locking devices which when clamped down, made it watertight and made the man inside a virtual prisoner until someone outside released him. It was ringed with six tiny glass peepholes no larger than half dollars through which the surrounding waters could be viewed, from about the same perspective as that of a swimmer treading water.

In the earliest trials Bushnell's brother was to do most of the operating. As the solid little craft was lowered into the water for the first time, both brothers showed their relief. The *Turtle* floated at just about the level David had estimated it would. The tiny hatch was opened. David's brother squeezed in through the narrow opening and lowered himself to the bottom deck built just over the lead ballast and the two flood tanks. The *Turtle* sank lower, but since the flood tanks were now filled with air, she still had plenty of freeboard above the water's gently rippling surface. Inside was a small seat projecting from one side so the operator could half sit as he worked a set of devices that were rather complicated for such a pipsqueak vessel.

The problem of the air supply was one Bushnell

had experimented with at great length. Not much was then known about breathing in a submerged vessel, but he estimated that the *Turtle*'s air capacity was enough to keep the operator conscious and active for thirty minutes. Since the submarine could make only two miles an hour and would not go far before her operator became winded, David Bushnell worked out a practical plan. For making her approach on an enemy ship the *Turtle* would proceed with her seven inches of conning tower just out of water and of course clamped. On the sides of the conning tower were the world's first recorded snorkel devices, two air tubes an inch in diameter, bent at the top in a U shape and containing cork float valves that closed them off the instant they went under water or were struck by a wave. These were almost exact prototypes of the present snorkel devices used by skin divers.

David Bushnell's first trials with the *Turtle* were remarkably successful. This was partly because he had worked out his plans with great mathematical precision and partly because he was so determined his patriotic invention should not fail that he provided every safety feature he could devise. The air tubes had inner safety valves operable by hand in the event the float valves failed or became jammed with floating seaweed. The force pumps had an extra set of valves in case of leakage through the primary set. The release catch for the 200 pounds of lead ballast was so placed that the operator could lay hand on it instantly. And there was even a set of crude navigational instruments installed.

The *Turtle* had a compass and she had a depth gauge. "On a clear day" the light filtering under water and through the tiny portholes made them readable "at a depth of three fathoms." Just to be safe, Bushnell affixed a chunk of fox fire—decaying wood with luminescent fungi growing on it—near these instruments so that they could be read at night. He had first tried a candle, then decided it consumed too much oxygen and also might be visible as a glow through the portholes when the vessel was surfaced. The depth gauge was a crude affair, a cork in a glass tube, which rose one inch for every fathom that the submarine submerged. Another, and less desirable, "depth gauge" was discovered after several trials: as soon as the *Turtle's* keel reached 3 fathoms (a mere 18 feet) the tar in her seams would start oozing through because of the water pressure on the outside. Needless to say, this was disconcerting to the operator, who found it difficult indeed to trim the tanks so that the craft remained hidden a few feet under the surface but did not descend to the dangerous tar-squeezing depth.

The trials were unexpectedly interrupted when David Bushnell's brother became ill and was unable to participate. David himself lacked the necessary physical agility and strength to work the craft. But in the spring of 1776 the unhappy defeats of the struggling Colonists brought the *Turtle* into prominence when Brigadier General Samuel Parsons of Lyme, commander of a brigade of Connecticut Continentals, heard about Bushnell's submarine.

"Find three volunteers for extra hazardous duty," he ordered, "and have them report to me at once." The military situation was critical. General Sir William Howe, by land, and Admiral Lord Richard Howe, by sea, brothers by kinship as well as purpose, were about to tighten the British noose about their biggest prize—Long Island and Manhattan. General Washington had no fleet to counteract the invasion. His only hope of disrupting the plans of the redcoats lay in great ingenuity and stealth.

Among the three volunteers was Sergeant Ezra Lee, also of Lyme, a strong, determined soldier who had acquitted himself well and was afraid of nothing on land or sea (or under it for that matter). He brought with him one further qualification—patience. Sergeant Lee was ordered to report to David Bushnell for training in the *Turtle*.

All during the late spring and early summer Lee bent to his historic task. Time and again he and the oak-ribbed craft almost sank forever to the muddy bottom of the Connecticut River, despite the fact that Bushnell had carefully secured a heavy cable to the boat to pull her to safety in the event of accident. And time and again Bushnell hauled the *Turtle* from the water to effect repairs or make further modifications in her complex gear. Sergeant Lee weathered the endless ordeal with patience. He so badly wanted his crack at the British fleet, by now infiltrating every bay and river along the New York coast, that he was willing to wait until every last contingency had been considered and provided for.

By late August, 1776, orders came through that Sergeant Lee and the *Turtle* were to be put to the ultimate test. The British had captured most of Long Island and the fleet lay in New York harbor off two other positions recently taken, Staten Island and Governor's Island. The arrival in Manhattan of the *Turtle*, transported by wagon, came as no surprise to the American leaders. Many months beforehand, John Adams had received a letter stating: "The famous water machine from Connecticut is every day expected in Camp. It must unavoidably be a clumsy business as its weight is about a ton."

The *Turtle* was given several preliminary trials in the Hudson River, but there was nothing more Bushnell could do to develop his boat. By this time he had spent what little money he had on her, and there were few men in the entire Continental Army who would have given any kind of American craft—undersea or otherwise—much chance against the mighty British fleet. Then, on the evening of September 6, the submarine attack was launched.

At Whitehall Stairs, near the Battery at the tip of Manhattan, a small group of Continental officers and men proceeded quietly down to the water's edge, their way lighted only by the pale light of a half-moon. Two miles away, directly to the southwest, lay the hated

British fleet. Somewhere among the men-of-war was the *Eagle*, Admiral Lord Howe's flagship under the command of one Captain Duncan.

"Has the underwater machine arrived yet?" several asked, speaking in tense whispers. "We do not have much time."

"She is here. Cast your eyes between those two whaleboats."

As the men reached the water they could see her now, and those who were viewing her for the first time gasped in amazement. She was not the whalelike contraption they had imagined, but a harmless-looking bit of flotsam that might have been a fancy wine cask afloat, topped by some kind of metal appendage. From this projected the head, arms and shoulders of a burly-looking man in a soldier's stocking cap. This must be the much-talked-about Sergeant Lee, a dauntless soldier who but for the grace of God should even now have been beneath a patriot's headstone for all the risks he had taken.

"There is more to this than meets the eye," quipped one officer, studying the proceedings with some skepticism.

"Aye," replied a companion seriously, "for why else would Major General Israel Putnam himself be on hand?" It was true, the figure of the General could be discerned in the moonlight, silently watching and inwardly praying. Perhaps more than any one else, save Washington, he knew the implications of the recent defeat of the American troops on Long Island. One could not expect miracles from a lone soldier in a tar-impregnated barrel; but one could hope.

"Are you ready, Ezra?"

"Aye. The gunpowder is securely affixed. The inside is, for the moment at least, dry. And I am aching to awaken Admiral Lord Howe with a peal of American thunder such as he has not heard before."

"We take you in tow then, and God be with us."

"How runs the tide?"

"At the ebb," came the subdued reply from an officer in one of the whaleboats. "It is about one glass to the turning, at which time you should be in the middle of the British fleet."

"Good," replied Lee, "then let us be away and to our task."

The plan was for the two whaleboats to tow the *Turtle* as close to the anchored ships as they dared without risking detection. They would then be able to select the *Eagle*—or, failing that, the *Asia*, another important man-of-war—and help direct Lee to the attack. The *Turtle* would remain on the surface until ready to separate from her two escorts, at which time the men in one of the whaleboats would batten down the hinged hatch cover.

Lee knew that his chances of escaping unaided from the craft in the event of accident were slim when the hatch finally was closed a few inches over his head and the oarsmen silently began rowing back to Whitehall Stairs. But the impact of his danger did not reach him fully until fifteen minutes later. Then, with only the conning tower above the surface, Sergeant Lee saw that he was approaching the dark silhouettes of the British ships with unexpected speed, even though he cranked the horizontal propeller shaft only enough to give him proper steerage.

Someone had made a disastrous error: the *outgoing tide was not about to turn at all!* Instead of slowing down, it was carrying him past the British ships. In desperation, Lee headed his craft north and cranked vigorously to try to buck the outward current. For two hours, with his strength waning and his arms aching he fought a losing battle. Then, when it seemed that his only choice was to drift well south of British-held Staten Island and try to make a more friendly shore, the tide began to turn.

Anyone else might have felt that he had answered a call far beyond his normal duty and been content to drift back to Whitehall and postpone the attack. But Lee had waited too long for this opportunity. Cautiously, his physical aches ignored in the excitement of contemplating the enemy, he headed for the vessel he thought was the *Eagle*. The tiny *Turtle* responded so quietly that he was able to move almost under the overhanging stern. Though he could hear the voices of sentries on deck when he cocked his ear to the air tubes, he remained undetected.

Lee had to move fast now. Through the portholes he could glimpse the first patches of gray to the east. Dawn would soon be on hand. He closed the valves in the air tubes, and pressed the foot pedals carefully. Underneath his feet, he could hear the sound of water streaming into the flood tanks. Inches at a time, the *Turtle* sank, as Lee put to good use all of his months of training in the Connecticut River. He watched the ripples lap at the porthole glass, barely flecked with gray light from the oncoming dawn. Then, as darkness closed above him, he released the foot pedals, cranked the propeller which would pull the craft forward under the heavy hull of the man-of-war, and pushed his face close to the compass and depth gauge.

Half a fathom . . . one fathom . . . he could barely make out the cork marking the depth as the fox fire glowed feebly. At two and a half fathoms, Lee decided he was deep enough and far enough under the rounded hull to attach the torpedo. Quickly he operated the two force pumps with his hands to eject the ballast water. The *Turtle* began to rise as her weight lessened. In a minute there came a sudden jar as the submarine jammed the vertical auger screw against the underside of the man-of-war. Lee pumped out more water to make sure he held a solid contact, then began turning the auger crank furiously.

It was several moments before Sergeant Lee realized the discouraging truth: the screw was not biting in at all—the ship's hull had been sheathed with copper to protect it from barnacles. For half an hour he maneuvered the tiny *Turtle* under the hull, seeking a vulnerable spot. There was none. He even tried submerging the *Turtle* to the greatest depth he dared, three fathoms. Then he pumped the flood tanks furiously, hoping the sudden rise of the craft would force the point to penetrate the metal. But the copper was too thick.

By this time the air supply was almost gone and Lee was groggy. He headed northeast by compass, cranking as vigorously as he could to escape the area, and then surfaced once more. Putting his face close to the air tubes, he unscrewed the safety valves and gulped in draughts of fresh sea air. It was not until he had revived fully that he realized with alarm that dawn had come and a new danger loomed. The turning tide was carrying him toward his goal now—Whitehall Stairs—but it was also swinging him too far to the east, toward British-held Governor's Island.

As Lee began wearily cranking again, he saw through the peepholes that he had been spotted. Several hundred Britishers lined the shore, their officers observing the submarine through glasses. Within a few minutes a twelve-oared barge put out from shore, headed straight for the *Turtle*. Capture was imminent since the rowers could easily overtake the *Turtle*. And Lee could no longer submerge because the air in his floating coffin was so foul that only what he sucked in through the breathing tubes kept him from passing out.

Closer and closer the barge came, with a man in the bow holding his musket ready to shoot, expecting some kind of Yankee trick. When the barge was only 60 yards away, Sergeant Lee decided to risk his own life rather than be captured. At least, he might take a barge-load of redcoats along with him. He released the catch that held the torpedo of gunpowder.

Instantly the clock mechanism started ticking away with the timer set for twenty minutes. The *Turtle* heeled slightly as she became separated from her torpedo, and the two drifted slightly apart. Then something unexpected happened.

On board the barge, the British became wary. Where there had been only one mysterious vessel, there now appeared to be two, moving independently. The barge commander gave a sudden order. His oarsmen backed on their oars, then swung the craft around and headed toward shore. They were not going to be caught by some rebel device.

Watching the British retreat, Lee knew that even his suicide plan had failed. Now he had to save his own life. The lethal machine drifted along with the tide, ticking ominously only a few yards from the *Turtle*. Furiously, Lee began cranking the propeller, all the time gasping for air and fighting off the dizziness that was upon him. Slowly the distance widened between the *Turtle* and the torpedo. But Lee's strength was draining fast.

At Whitehall Stairs, General Israel Putnam and the little group of patriots were in despair over Lee's fate. When dawn broke with no indication of the *Turtle*'s whereabouts, the best the Americans could hope for was that Lee had made shore safely somewhere south of Staten Island and hidden his vessel where it could be salvaged later. Then, in the early light, they had seen the commotion a little more than a mile away on Governor's Island and watched the British barge putting out, hesitating and returning. Could the activity have anything to do with the *Turtle?*

Sergeant Lee had been trained well for his historic assignment. He managed to put safe distance between him and the floating torpedo. Suddenly, some twenty minutes after release, when it had drifted to a point just north of Governor's Island, the 130 pounds of gunpowder went off exactly as David Bushnell had calculated it would, "with a tremendous explosion, throwing up large bodies of water to an immense height."

By this time the patriots realized the mission had failed and that Lee was making his way safely to Whitehall. But the force of the explosion was so great as it echoed across the bay that General Putnam cried out in his curious way, "God curse 'em! That'll do it for 'em!" And the patriots at Whitehall cheered.

The whaleboats rushed out to aid the exhausted Lee, open the hatch and tow the *Turtle* to shore. Thus ended the first of several forays made by the little undersea craft against the British. All of these were termed tactically unsuccessful, but they did their part toward making the British more respectful of patriot ingenuity and valor. And the *Turtle,* unlike many of the more elaborate submarines of the following century, never once carried an operator to the horrible death of suffocating in an escapeless tomb beneath the sea.

Of the inventiveness of Bushnell, the courage of Lee and the first submarine attack in history, George Washington wrote in a letter to Thomas Jefferson many years later, "I then thought and still think it was an effort of genius."

Aboard a Nuclear Sub

by
Commander
James Calvert

It is a far cry from David Bushnell's first rudimentary craft to the huge and deadly weapon powered by atomic fission. A host of inventors, including such men as John P. Holland and Simon Lake, contributed ever more complex and efficient designs and methods of propulsion. These culminated in the launching of the submarine Nautilus *in January, 1954. In one important sense, the* Nautilus *was the first truly undersea craft. Previous submarines had been forced to surface from time to time to recharge batteries. Sometimes, with enemy vessels in the vicinity, this handicap could mean the difference between survival and death. But with nuclear power a submarine can remain submerged literally for months.*

The nuclear sub was in large part the brain child

of the then Captain Hyman George Rickover, a naval officer who refused to take "no" for an answer. Against constant opposition from brassbound naval personnel and industrialists, he forced his conception through. Twice he was passed over for promotion to rear admiral, and the Navy's rule was "two times and out." The resultant storm forced a Navy Board to reconsider. He at last received his star, to which was later added a second.

The Nautilus and its even more efficient successors have accomplished almost unbelievable feats of navigation. The Triton, commanded by Edward Beach, circumnavigated the globe without once completely surfacing. The Skate, under Commander James Calvert, was ordered to sail under the Arctic ice pack and surface at the North Pole. His successful accomplishment of this assignment was the result of infinite care in planning every stage of the voyage. One of Commander Calvert's daily duties was to check routine from stem to stern. His description of such a tour gives a graphic picture of the duties of various members of the crew.

NEXT MORNING, as is my custom when we are at sea, I took a walk through the ship, visiting every habitable area from bow to stern. I learn all sorts of things on these trips—what shape a lot of the equipment is in, what small problems have arisen or are likely to arise, and (most important of all) what frame of mind the crew is in. I know of no other way for the skipper to get the feel of his ship.

Ever since I have been going to sea in the *Skate* people have been asking me what it is really like to go to sea in a nuclear submarine. I'm always tongue-tied by this question—there is so much to say. But I think the most striking and distinct difference from any other sort of seagoing is that one is free, completely free, from the surface of the sea.

The ancient curse of the seagoer is that strangely nauseating motion imparted to ships by the surface of the sea. For centuries, sailors (especially Navy men) have denied its existence; most would rather choke than admit that it affects them. But it does. Even men who have gone to sea all their lives and have long since gotten over any trace of seasickness, no matter what the weather, know the discomfort and fatigue that come from the surface of the sea. The British have an expressive term for it: *sea weariness.* And no one knows better what this means than those who take ordinary submarines to sea. Small and low in the water, they are miserable in rough weather and uncomfortable all the time. Forced to remain on or near the surface to get the air which their diesel engines consume in such huge quantities, they are always affected by the motion of the water.

In the *Skate,* however, we are breaking the long-established rules of sea travel. Our throbbing turbines receive their power from a source that has no need of oxygen or any other ingredient of the atmosphere.

Traveling 300 feet below the surface day after day, we are almost devoid of any sense of motion. Only the almost imperceptible vibration of our propellers reminds us we are moving. Consequently, to walk through the ship is like passing through a small, highly concentrated, self-sufficient city built deep underground, with mechanical instruments as its only link with the outside world.

Although she is a little shorter than a conventional U.S. diesel submarine, the *Skate* weighs—or, to use the proper naval term, displaces—almost half again as much. The difference is due to the greater hull diameter required to enclose the nuclear machinery. This, of course, allows more roomy and comfortable living conditions than those in conventional submarines. The elimination of the large storage battery and of the reserves of diesel fuel have also increased the space available for the crew.

The *Skate* is divided into two basic parts: the engineering spaces aft, and the control and living spaces forward. The extreme ends of the ship contain the torpedo tubes which are the only armament of the ship (she carries a total of twenty-two torpedoes and the tubes are always kept loaded). Each nest of tubes is serviced by a torpedo room which contains reload torpedoes and also, with characteristic economy of space, bunks and lockers for crewmen.

Almost in the exact center of the submarine is the reactor compartment. Here is located the uranium-packed atomic pile (the reactor) which provides the energy to drive the *Skate* tirelessly through the ocean depths. The reactor consists of a huge jug-shaped steel vessel, almost 20 feet high, containing a gridwork of metal-clad uranium plates. This vessel is filled with ordinary water under pressure so great that it cannot boil.

When control rods which fit into the uranium grid are pulled out to the correct positions, a controlled chain reaction of uranium fission takes place. This reaction generates heat throughout the uranium grid, which is transferred to the water surrounding it. This heated, heavily pressurized water is then circulated out of the reactor vessel, into the large cylinders of the steam generators. Here the pressurized water gives up some of its heat to another water system, at more conventional pressure, on the other side of a metal barrier. This secondary water, as it is called, turns to steam which is carried back to the engine room through heavy steel pipes. Here it spins the turbines which drive the ship and generate electric power for use on board.

The pressurized water, which is pumped in and out of the reactor every few seconds, is of course heavily radioactive. It does not, however, transmit this radioactivity to the secondary water even though it is in close contact with it in the steam generator. This is the key point in the safe operation of the power plant. The steam that goes aft to the engine room is not radioactive, and no special precautions need be taken with it. All of the radioactivity is confined to one compartment, which is safely shielded by lead plates and heavy sheets of polyethylene plastic.

Although no one can be in the compartment when the reactor is operating, this poses no obstacle to passage back and forth through the ship, as a properly shielded walkway is provided. Small round windows of heavy leaded glass are provided so that the crewmen can check conditions in the reactor from time to time.

I began my tour by walking aft through the control center and into the shielded passageway of the reactor compartment. It is necessary for me to stoop my six feet two slightly as I walk along the 30-foot passageway between the gleaming banks of stainless-steel piping. The reactor is below the floor, the only evidence of its presence a faint hum from the giant centrifugal pumps which circulate pressurized water through the grid of the reactor. The waxlike smell of warm polyethylene filled the air. I stooped to lift the metal cover from one of the inspection windows in the deck of the tunnel-like passageway. Almost 20 feet below me I could see the actual bottom of the well-lighted, deserted reactor-machinery space. All looked in good order; replacing the metal cover, I passed on into the engine room.

Passing several banks of instruments, each as large as an upright piano, I came to the two turbine-generator sets that produce electricity for this city beneath the sea. They are the heart of the ship, manufacturing not only electrical power for lighting, cooking, heating, and air purification, but also the electricity required to control the reactor and to operate the main power plant itself. If these whirring giants should fail us, the *Skate* would soon become a lifeless hulk.

The engine room is lighted in every corner with fluorescent lamps. The gray machinery, black rubber decking, and copper piping combine in a cool abstraction reminiscent of the paintings of Fernand Léger. As I passed, the young men standing by the turbines —probably a little self-conscious in my presence— seemed as efficient and impersonal as the machines they were tending.

I continued aft into the maneuvering room, actually an instrument-filled corner of the engine room which serves as the control center for the power plant. Fred O'Brien, a man of about thirty whose broad face and smiling brown eyes betray his national heritage, sat in front of a panel covered with dials and gauges. One quivering black needle displayed the power level of the nuclear reactor; others showed the temperature of the water passing in and out of the reactor, its pressure, and the velocity of its flow. As O'Brien kept attentive watch on all these meters, he manipulated a small pistol switch that governed the movement of the control rods. With this switch he occasionally ran the reactor rods slowly in or out to control the flow of its power. Next to him sat Wayne Winans, a short, stocky electrician, giving the same close attention to a similar board which contained the meters and controls for *Skate*'s complex electrical system. Beside him, standing over the two steam throttles, one for each propeller shaft, another man stood ready to obey any signal from the control center.

In over-all charge of these men, and of the whole engine room, was Lieutenant Bill Cowhill. He stood back from the control panels so that he could see all of the instruments without moving. Bill is a thin, crew-cut young man who seems to exude calm and capability in all directions. His uniform always seems to be pressed, his shoes always shined. He nodded to me as I entered, carefully knocked the ash from his cigarette, and after a glance at the panels before him wrote down several entries in his engineering log in a neat draftsman's hand.

Bill had served with me in my first submarine command, the *Trigger*. He came from Northwestern University, class of 1950, a product of the NROTC program. I well remembered asking him what he had majored in at Northwestern; I was somewhat taken aback to learn that it had been English literature. However it soon become apparent that a knowledge of Shakespeare and Hemingway did not necessarily preclude a lot of knowledge about naval matters. I was particularly happy when, during his tour in the *Trigger*, Bill decided to remain in the Navy as a career officer. Later he was selected for training in nuclear power and graduated second in his class from the Navy's nuclear school at New London.

The maneuvering room is the nerve center for the propulsion plant as the control center forward is for the ship as a whole. When matters are going routinely the maneuvering room is a pretty peaceful place. But when an emergency of any sort occurs—a fire, steam leak, uncontrolled flooding—many things must be done rapidly and accurately in the maneuvering room to prevent serious damage to the power plant and the rest of the ship. It is at this time that the training and presence of mind of men such as these may make the difference between safety and disaster.

Then I thought ahead a few days, visualizing this same group at work in the same space—but with the knowledge that overhead stretched an infinite canopy of ice. Would they be able to work with the same cool efficiency?

I flipped through a metal binder behind Bill Cowhill's shoulder. Here were posted the emergency bills for quick reference in any emergency. The first was *fire*. Fire is an age-old dread of the seagoer, but it is particularly dangerous to the submarine, with its confined spaces and limited air supply. The menace of heat and flames aside, the atmosphere of a submarine, once fouled by smoke, becomes poisonous to breathe until renewed with fresh air. I noticed the first item on the list of actions to be taken in event of fire: STAND BY TO SURFACE.

I flipped to the next casualty bill: *steam leak*. The engine room of the *Skate* is filled with hundreds of feet of looping, twisting pipe that carry steam to the turbines, to the fresh-water-producing evaporator, and to hissing air ejectors that maintain a vacuum in the condensers which collect the exhaust steam from the turbines. A leak in any of this piping could fill the engine room with billowing clouds of searing steam. The men in the engine room would not have long to live unless the first step on the emergency bill could be executed without delay: STAND BY TO SURFACE.

The next bill was also one peculiar to nuclear submarines—*radiation leak.* In the event that any of the piping carrying the heavily pressurized water circulating in and out of the reactor should begin to leak, clouds of highly radioactive steam would result, again with dire results unless the ship could be brought to the surface and the air renewed.

The next bill was tabbed with red: *collision.* No newcomer was this one. As long as men have gone under the sea in submarines, they have feared collision. An ordinary egg lowered into the sea can, because of the strength inherent in its shape, go to amazing depths before it shatters from the pressure of the sea. The same egg, however, will fracture if given even the slightest of blows with a sharp implement. A submarine hull is much the same. Constructed to withstand the all-encompassing squeeze of the sea at considerable depths, it will rupture easily when struck by an unyielding object. The internal construction of the submarine is such, moreover, that almost no one has an opportunity to escape. A special alarm is installed in each submarine for only one purpose—to warn of imminent collision. It is a piercing, whining, crescendo that splits the ears and strikes instinctive fear into the marrow of those who hear it.

The history of submarines in all navies over the past fifty years is sprinkled with horror stories originating with collision. On a misty evening in 1925 the American submarine *S–51* was lazing along on the surface near Block Island, the same waters *Skate* had traveled as she left New London. Without warning the looming bow of a large merchant ship appeared out of the mist. There was nothing the captain of the *S–51* could do. Seconds later the black bow ripped into the tiny sub and sent her careening to the bottom. Only the two or three men on the bridge lived to tell the story.

Two years later, on a stormy gray-clouded afternoon in mid-December 1927, another American submarine, the *S–4*, was conducting engineering trials near the summer-resort village of Provincetown on Cape Cod. The captain was ready to surface and raised his periscope for a quick sweep around to ensure that all was clear. His face froze in horror and disbelief as he saw the gray sides and foaming bow wave of a destroyer so close that collision was inevitable. A crack like that of an artillery piece echoed through the *S–4* as the destroyer's knifelike bow struck her amidships. Heeling at a sickening angle, the submarine plunged to the bottom of Cape Cod Bay as the icy water gushed in. Six men lived for nearly three days in that black tomb on the bottom, tapping signals, but they were never to see the daylight again.

Collision disasters, however, were not restricted to the past. Only a few months before we had left New

London, another American submarine, the *Stickleback*, had been conducting training exercises at sea near Pearl Harbor. A mistake in the internal control of the submarine put her near the surface in the path of the speeding escort vessel with whom she was working. The propellers of the surface ship churned the water in a vain effort to stop as her bow sliced into the *Stickleback*'s side. Fortunately the captain of the submarine was able to surface his ship and evacuate it before she plunged to the bottom in water thousands of feet deep.

The *Skate* would be meeting few ships where she was going, nor would she have to run the risks of shallow water in the deep polar sea. But there would be something even more dangerous—ice. Ice can be as hard and unyielding on impact as steel; its edges can stab through the hull of a ship like a sliver of glass slashes paper. At least one famous ship, with far more protection against sinking than we, had been brought to doom by the power of ice. The "unsinkable" *Titanic* had been ripped open and sunk by the submerged spur of an iceberg. No one knew for certain what sharp contact with the ice might do to the eggshell hull of a submarine. No one wanted to find out. At any rate, in the event of submerged collision, the first step was the familiar STAND BY TO SURFACE.

For the submarine in trouble, the surface is synonymous with safety. But there would be no surface for us. Whatever occurred, we would be forced to take care of ourselves inside this all-too-fragile steel-cased bubble of air.

My next stop was the aftermost compartment of the ship, the stern room. At the extreme end are the bank of vaultlike doors of the stern torpedo tubes. Nested on either side of the compartment, interspersed with spare torpedoes, are bunks and lockers for fifteen men. In one forward corner of the room is the ship's laundry, complete with a home-style electric drier. In the other corner is a small laboratory where tests are conducted to ensure that the nuclear reactor is operating properly and that its radioactivity is at a safe level. In the laboratory I saw the ship's medical officer, Lieutenant Dick Arnest, at work "reading" one of the film badges that each member of the crew is required to wear. (The undeveloped film is sensitive to nuclear radiation; the degree to which it turns dark upon development indicates to the doctor how much radiation the wearer has received.) Dr. Arnest keeps records of the total amount of radiation received by each member of the crew. It is interesting to note that the man with the highest recorded amount of radiation has received less than he would in a single set of dental X rays.

It was apparent that *Skate* would find it difficult to shoot any torpedoes from her stern tubes in a hurry. Set up in front of them was a working oceanographic laboratory. Wooden boxes full of empty bottles for water samples were everywhere. On a bench was mounted a spectrometer to measure the index of refraction (ability to bend light) of sea water, and other complicated-looking instruments were all around. In the midst of these gadgets was our senior civilian scientist, oceanographer Dr. Gene LaFond of San Diego. The doctor, a cheerful white-haired man of fifty or so, was to establish himself as an absolutely ruthless poker player at our Saturday afternoon sessions.

Dr. LaFond is also quite a bridge player. He and Mrs. LaFond spent a few years in India, where the doctor taught oceanography. Bridge was a favorite faculty pastime, and the LaFonds were regular participants. The doctor, however, is a man of independent mind and he resented the complete subjection of all the players to one of two bridge systems, each of them invented by men unknown to him. What was more, the players—particularly Dr. LaFond's wife, who was usually his partner—seemed to resent the fact that he was not an adherent of any recognized system. He remedied this lack by writing a bridge book of his own, complete with elaborate point system and complex rules of play. However, when any given chapter reached the point of concrete advice—what bid to make or what card to play—it was always the same: *Play it by ear.* The book (printed at the doctor's own expense), was emblazoned *The LaFond System* and was replete with enthusiastic reviews—all written by Hindi.

I left the doctor adjusting his spectroscope and

retraced my steps forward through the engine room and into the forward part of the ship. A conventional submarine is divided laterally into two layers, the lower one of which is normally used for storage. The extra-large hull diameter of *Skate* enables her to be divided into three layers. This creates two living levels and one storage level, with much more space all around. The upper level contains the control center and the officers' wardroom and quarters; the lower level holds the crew's mess hall, bunkroom, galley, and washrooms.

The crew's mess hall is literally never idle. As I entered it, about a dozen of the crew were sitting about reading magazines, playing cards, and studying. The mess hall must serve as a reading room, dining room, study hall, classroom, movie theater, and general lounge for the entire crew of eighty-seven men. It is equipped with its own Coke machine (paper-cup variety) and a hi-fi system which plays either from a juke-box selector or a tape recorder. (The radiomen often tape a news broadcast in the radio room when the ship is at the surface for a few minutes and then bring it to the mess hall where it can be played at leisure.) Just outside the mess hall is located an automatic ice-cream machine. And—of course—in one corner stands a gleaming coffee urn, providing an inexhaustible supply of that essential elixir of Navy life.

I sat down for a moment beside Chief Torpedoman Paul Dornberg, our chief of the boat. He is the man in direct military charge of the crew. The assignment of watches, the assignment of bunks and lockers, the cleanliness of uniforms, the orderliness of the mess hall, the training of new men in the fundamentals of going to sea—all of these are Paul Dornberg's concern. He is well suited for the job. A strapping, vigorous man of about forty, he can be immediately recognized by his luxuriant handlebar mustache. He is also a strict Lutheran, an equally strict teetotaler, and a rabid supporter of the Cleveland Indians.

"Well, Chief," I asked, "have you found a bunk for everyone?"

"Not without looking in all the corners, Captain," Dornberg said. "You know we have better than a hundred people on board with the civilians. Going to have over thirty of them hotbunking—but we didn't promise to bring them *Queen Mary* style!"

Hotbunking is the Navy term for the sharing of a bunk by two men or, more often, of two bunks by three men. Then, when one of them is on watch, the other two can sleep. It's not the best of arrangements, but it works if everyone cooperates.

I stepped forward into the galley. Walled and equipped in stainless steel, with a white tile deck, this compact room, not more than 12 feet square, contains all the equipment necessary to turn out more than three hundred full meals every day. In addition, the galley prepares sizable snacks for the men who are going on, or just coming off, the night watches. The rest of the night is spent baking for the next day.

In charge of this culinary beehive is a tall cook

named Ray Aten. Despite the frequent professional nibbling which sadly tends to expand the girth of Navy cooks, Ray seems to have no trouble staying trim. It may be that the rigors of his job—which he performs most conscientiously and skillfully—help to keep him in fighting shape.

The delightful aroma of roasting pork filled the air. Aten leaned over to look into the ovens and basted one of the browning roasts. They looked as good as they smelled. "For lunch?" I asked.

"Yes, sir, along with mashed potatoes and broccoli," Aten answered with a smile.

Aten has three assistants but they were nowhere in evidence this morning; he was preparing the meal all alone. Due to the smallness of the galley, the cooks take turns with the meals, staying completely out of the affair when it is not theirs. The cook preparing the meal is always assisted by two junior crew members designated mess cooks—the polite Navy designation for kitchen police. The same food is served in the officers' wardroom and the mess hall, so every meal eaten in the *Skate* is prepared in this small room.

The preparation of meals is not the end of Ray Aten's problems, however. Whenever a Navy ship goes to sea there is always the possibility that it will be necessary to keep her there longer than originally planned. For this reason it is Navy policy to carry on board submarines enough food for sixty days, whatever the planned length of the cruise. This meant that Aten had been required to store enough food on board the *Skate* for 18,000 meals when we left New London. This demands more than a little ingenuity.

The third, or lowest, layer in the forward part of the *Skate*'s hull is mainly devoted to this problem. Large shelved rooms hold canned goods, flour, sugar, coffee, and other staples. Other spaces provide cold storage for eggs, butter, vegetables, and fruit, while still others act as deep freezes for meat and frozen foods. The purchasing and proper storage of all this before a cruise—often with very little advance warning—is the sole responsibility of the chief cook.

Aten has one other seemingly minor but absolutely essential responsibility. A ship that travels submerged day after day must have some means of getting rid of its garbage. In the corner of the alley stands a heavy bronze tube about four feet high, with a top like that of a pressure cooker. Several times a day garbage and trash are put in nylon mesh bags like ordinary shopping bags. The cooks remove the top from the tube and drop the filled bags into it—it holds about four. The tube reaches all the way to a door in the bottom of the ship. When the top is tightly fastened, the bottom door is opened and the nylon bags are pumped out into the sea. An automatic lock prevents opening both doors at once—an accident that would be fatal to the ship.

The bags must be weighted in order to drop out of the tube properly and to prevent them from floating and thus betraying the submarine's presence in wartime. Bricks are used for this purpose; another of Ray Aten's loading problems is stowing one thousand bricks for the garbage ejector; this is the number of bags of trash and garbage that may be pumped out of the ship on a sixty-day patrol.

I stepped out of the galley, across a narrow passageway, and into the main bunkroom. Here, in a room about 30 feet long and 15 feet wide, are bunks and lockers for forty-one men. This is made possible, with reasonable comfort, by a most efficient use of space. The bunks are in tiers four high. Each bunk is isolated on three sides by sheet-metal barriers, provided with its own ventilation supply, and equipped with an individual reading light. The mattresses and pillows are foam rubber. A small shoe locker is provided at the foot of each bunk, and larger lockers are built into the walls of the room.

At this hour the bunkroom was largely deserted. Only a few men, probably those who had stood the midwatch (midnight to 4 A.M.) were sleeping. A room with this many men living in it is either kept scrupulously neat or it becomes a hopeless shambles. Paul Dornberg sees to it that the first of these two alternatives is followed on the *Skate*. He had, however, made one concession to the storage problems of Ray Aten. The floor of each passageway was completely covered with a single layer of bricks. A cover of plywood had been neatly cut to fit over the bricks, making a smooth and dust-free surface. The ingenuity of submarine sailors in finding storage space is famous, but I had to admit that this went beyond the usual limits.

Closing the bunkroom door (which is lightproof and soundproof to keep out distraction) I walked forward into the *Skate*'s torpedo room. At the far end of the room gleamed the bronze breech doors of the forward torpedo tubes. Along each side were racked the long, cigar-shaped torpedoes. Twenty bunks are strategically located throughout this large room, some of them among the torpedoes.

In charge was Torpedoman Julian Buckley, a fresh-faced, stocky New Englander. He and a group of his assistants were busy with a torpedo which had been pulled into the middle of the room and opened like a giant robot patient on an operating table. Navy philosophy about torpedoes is the same as that concerning food: *Be ready*. No matter what the submarine's mission, a certain number of torpedoes are carried on board. Continual checks are performed to assure that they are in working order. This was what Buckley and his men were doing. Armed with flashlights, tools, and meters, they performed intricate maneuvers deep within the weapon. I doubt that any group of surgeons more earnestly discussed a problem over an open patient, although the language in this case may have been somewhat more colorful.

"Good morning, Captain," Buckley said as he stood up and wiped his brow.

"Good morning. How does this load of fish look—are they in good shape?" I returned.

"Too soon to say, Captain, we've only looked at two of them, but you know how it is—those shops don't take care of them the way they used to."

I smiled, thinking to myself that Buckley, even on one of the world's newest and finest ships, was not immune to the Navy custom of believing that, somehow, things were better in the old days.

"I know you'll have 'em in top shape in a few days," I laughed as I left.

From the forward torpedo room I walked back through the mess hall, up a broad metal stairway (a luxury in place of the narrow ladders usual in submarines) to the control center and into the officers' wardroom. This room serves as combination office, lounge, and dining room, corresponding to the mess hall for the crew. It was now nearly lunch time; a crisp white cloth was on the table, set with shining silver and the plain, blue-trimmed earthenware that has been traditional in Navy wardrooms for over a hundred years.

Our head steward, Woodrow Wilson Jones, was just putting salad on the table and ensuring that everything was in readiness. He then called the officers for lunch; before long we were enjoying delicious roast pork as the *Skate* moved along at 18 knots without noticeable motion, 300 feet below the stormy surface of the Atlantic Ocean.

The *Skate* was a magnificent ship. Everything that human ingenuity and the resources of the nation could provide had been included in her construction. No submariner had ever sailed in such comfort and luxury. Indeed, the ship itself tended to lull one into a sense of complete security—the Arctic and its frozen wastes seemed far outside our world.

And yet, every turn of our propellers brought us nearer our goal. Nearer regions for which the *Skate* had not been designed, regions fraught with danger for this ship upon which our lives depended.

Although none of us on board knew for certain what lay ahead of us, we knew that both the *Skate* and her men were facing the challenge of their lives.

SEVEN MILES DOWN

by
Jacques Piccard and
Robert S. Dietz

Even the nuclear submarine has its limitations. There is one dimension, the vertical, which it has not yet conquered. Beyond certain depths the enormous pressure of the water would crack the hull like a peanut shell. To reach the greatest depths, specially designed and reinforced bodies are required. The first successful craft of this sort was a spherical steel chamber designed by the biologist William Beebe and Otis Barton, which they called a bathysphere. In it they sank over half a mile beneath the seas off Bermuda in 1934. The bathysphere was connected with a mother ship by a steel cable and had no means of locomotion in any direction. The method was improved on by Professor Auguste Piccard, who had previously made a record balloon ascent into the stratosphere. Once launched, Piccard's diving vessel, called a bathyscaphe, was independent of the mother ship. It sank when gasoline, which is lighter than water, was ejected. It rose by the release of iron shot attached to the hull by electromagnetism. In the bathyscaphe Trieste, *Auguste's son Jacques descended to the lowest known depths of the ocean, the mighty Challenger Deep in the Pacific, and in the following article he tells the story of the descent. But the bathyscaphe itself is not the final answer. It can maneuver only in a vertical direction. Others, such as Captain Cousteau, are experimenting to overcome this handicap. The United States Government is planning a small atomic submarine that will be able to explore the ocean bottom, particularly the continental shelf, where oil and mineral deposits await discovery and where schools of fish can be tracked.*

I TRIED TO SLEEP that night but with little success. The *Wandank* rolled and pitched. She was taking blue water across her bow. I was concerned about the fragile *Trieste* riding on 600 feet of cable at our stern. The 200-mile tow had been—to use an American phrase—a "rough go."

The long tow down from Guam had started off well. Running before the seas, we had made four knots during the first day. It appeared that we could make the big dive on the third day. But then the towline parted. We lost precious hours. We could not be on our station by first light of the third day. Then another day was scratched when the *Wandank* was unable to tow at more than one knot against towering head seas to spot us on the precise diving point. These delays stirred up anxieties.

I could tell myself that this was just another dive. It wasn't, of course, and I knew it. First of all, this dive would be my farewell—my valedictory—to the bathyscaphe *Trieste*. If all went well, I would return to Switzerland and lay the plans for a new underwater vehicle. Secondly, in the morning we would attempt a descent into the deepest hole in the deepest ocean—the Challenger Deep.

All through that stormy night the team of scientists aboard the destroyer escort sought to pinpoint that deepest hole with TNT charges. They were still making explosive soundings when I went on deck in the predawn of Dive Day, Saturday, January 23, 1960. A mile astern I could make out the lights of the destroyer escort, the *USS Lewis DE 635*, as the big seas lifted her above the ragged horizon.

A shuddering KER-UMP signaled the eight hundredth attempt to sound that big hole. A plume of white water shot into the sky.

(I learned later that our delay in diving was actually fortunate. It gave the *Lewis* sufficient time to find the very deepest part of the Challenger Deep. The special "PDR" echo sounder on the *Lewis* [an Edo with a TimeFax Precision Recorder] proved unequal to the task of surveying this ultradeep bottom. The slow and tedious method of sounding explosion was resorted to. Just a few hours prior to our dive the *Lewis* detailed a 4 by 1-mile slot with an echo delay time of 14 seconds, indicating a depth of about 5,950 fathoms.)

The descent was originally scheduled for 0700. With the bad weather, it was dangerous to board before daylight. So I set it for 0800. The seas had not moderated perceptibly. If anything, the trade winds had freshened. Conditions didn't look auspicious. Should everything be risked under these circumstances? This was the decision I'd have to make soon.

Lieutenant Shumaker and Giuseppe Buono joined me on the fantail. Flares had been dropped from the *Lewis*. The *Wandank* was wallowing toward them. No doubt now. The flares were the X that marked the spot—directly below was the basement of the world. As the distance between the two ships closed, I could make out the dye markers. The big moment was coming up fast.

It was still too dark to attempt to board the *Trieste*—we waited impatiently until 0715. A try was made at launching the project boat. It was impossible. Twenty-five-foot waves forced us to abandon the attempt. A rubber raft was pressed into service. It was a touch-and-go operation, but finally we managed to get it overside. We were seaborne, Lieutenant Shumaker, Buono, and I. But the final decision to dive or not to dive was still in the balance.

The sight that met my eyes when we boarded the

wallowing bathyscaphe was discouraging, to say the least. Broaching seas smothered her. The deck was a mess. Everything was awash. It was apparent at once that the tow from Guam had taken a terrific toll.

A hasty inspection revealed that the surface telephone (used for topside communication after we were sealed in the sphere) had been carried away. The tachometer (the instrument that measured our diving rate) was badly damaged and inoperative. The vertical current meter was dangling by a few wires.

I was worried. Buono showed it. "So? Do we dive, signor?"

I asked myself that same question. Was it sheer madness to dive seven miles into the sea under such conditions?

I looked across the angry seas and saw that Walsh was having a rough time getting seaborne from the *Lewis* in a motor whaleboat. He was on his way now. The whaleboat careened toward us. Walsh leaped aboard in good Navy style. Walsh grabbed a stanchion and the whaleboat peeled off to stand by.

Then he looked things over. He didn't like what he saw any better than I. He shook his head. "What do you think, Jacques?"

"I'll know better after I've checked below," I replied.

I swung into the conning tower, dropped down the ladder and eeled through the door into the sphere. First, I energized the electromagnets. All circuits were in order. I checked my watch. It was now 0800. The time factor was critical. If we were going to dive that day, we couldn't delay much longer. It was vital to accomplish the 14-mile round trip to the ocean floor and back before darkness.

If we didn't surface until after dark we might not be spotted. According to my very careful calculations we couldn't dive later than 0900 if we were to maintain a safe time margin. It is all very well for a man seeking adventure to take chances. I wasn't looking for adventure. I wanted a successful and uneventful operation. I wanted to leave nothing to chance.

Essentially things were in order. I made the decision. We would dive.

Topside, they were waiting for my report. All I had to do was nod. Walsh signaled his agreement. Buono clambered aft to disconnect the towline. I removed the pins that hold the ballast mechanically. Once removed, the shot was held by the electromagnets alone. I could now jettison ballast at will by cutting the current.

Feverish activity on deck occupied final precious moments. Walsh had slipped below to check a new electric thermometer. I called to Buono to see if he was ready.

"*E a posto tutto?*" ["*Is everything ready?*"]

"*O kappa, signor,*" Buono nodded, using the Italian version of okay.

It was 0810—full morning now. I took one last look at the sea and sky. The *Wandank* was standing off a quarter mile away rolling and pitching in the big swells. Still farther off was the *Lewis*, silhouetted against the heavy overcast. The tropical heat pressed down like a steamy blanket.

But there was no time for poetic contemplation. Quickly I gave Buono his last-minute instructions. Once we sealed the door he would flood the sas (the integral entrance tube that allows direct access to the cabin of the bathyscaphe when it is already afloat) and make final diving preparations. With communications from the sphere to topside out, we arranged a signal. If anything was amiss below I would switch on the motor and rotate the topside propellers.

Buono clasped hands with me and then Walsh. He wished us *buona fortuna* [good luck].

"*Grazie*" ["Thanks"], I answered. "*Arrivederci*" ["See you later"].

We swung closed the heavy steel door. We turned up the bolt that would seal us securely in our vault. The air was cool and dry in the sphere thanks to the silica gel. But the seas were buffeting the float, swinging our little spherical cell to and fro. I had but one thing on my mind: to dive as quickly as possible into the serene depths.

I checked my watch. It was now 0815. Quickly, I reviewed every essential detail. We were diving without some important instruments. I would have only my watch and my depth gauge with which to calculate our rate of descent. In a descent everything depends on buoyancy control; on conserving and expending ballast with a delicate and knowledgeable touch.

We had a total of 1,440 seconds of ballast; that is to say, I could jettison 25 pounds of iron shot per second for a total of, roughly, 16 long tons. That amount of ballast would do it, with a lot to spare.

Through the after porthole I could see water flooding the antechamber. I opened the oxygen valves and checked the air purification system. We could expect to dive momentarily. Had our tachometer been operative, the very instant of descent would have been apparent. As it was, we simply had to wait to see the pressure gauge moving.

I wanted to log that instant. My eyes were on my watch. Suddenly, at 0823, the rocking ceased, the sphere became calm. I glanced at the depth gauge. The needle was quivering.

We were on our way down. We were *entre deux eaux*, to use a French expression—in midwater. The *grande plongée* [great dive] had begun. I looked over at Walsh. We both sighed in relief.

Slowly we settled to 340 feet. There, at 0835, the descent was halted. In fact, we were slowly bounced upward several yards. This, of course, was the main thermocline, the cold water of increased density resisting our penetration.

We took this opportunity to recheck our instruments. My usual diving procedure was to wait for the gasoline to cool sufficiently to push on through this obstruction. On this dive there was no time to lose if we were to surface before nightfall. I valved off some gasoline from the maneuvering tank.

Once again we began settling—but only briefly. Again, at 370 feet, we were bounced upward. I pushed the gasoline valving switch once more. At 420 feet and again at 515 feet we were repulsed by the stubborn thermocline resistance. Never before in all of my sixty-five dives had I encountered so many strong thermal barriers. The little ascents were caused by internal waves which cause a constant rising and falling of the thermocline.

I did not know it then, of course, but another factor contributed to the slowness of our descent. The scaphe refused to sink when Buono flooded the air tanks in the float. She was slightly light due to the high temperature of the gasoline. So he opened up the sas hatch once more, letting waves wash in, completely filling it with water. Split-second agility was then needed to seal the hatch and jump into the raft before the scaphe sank. Normally, some air is left in the sas; as we sink this air is compressed, adding weight to the *Trieste*. With this air pocket missing, we were almost neutrally buoyant so that we came to rest on the slightest water density discontinuity.

Valuable time was consumed. At 0900 we had descended a mere 800 feet. There was a long way to go. Our average speed to this point was only 4 inches per second. At that snail's pace it would take more than thirty hours to complete our descent.

Now our sphere began to drop in earnest. We were

through the sea's twilight zone. Beyond the port there was darkness, but not yet total blackness. Descending into the sea, the night comes slowly like a northern dusk.

At 1,000 feet I switched off the cabin light for a careful look into the sea. A faint trace of light still seeped down from above. I could just barely see the outline of the after-shot tub.

I turned the cabin light on again. I tested the forward beam that casts a cone of light into the sea. The probing beam picked up a familiar illusion, familiar to me at least. Formless plankton appeared like a snowfall—only streaming upward instead of downward.

As we plummeted, there was an illusion of great speed. And we *were* falling fast—more than three feet per second (the speed of an average elevator). This was just about our terminal velocity.

Walsh tried the UQC acoustic telephone. His effort to contact the *Wandank* had been unavailing. Now, he made contact with the *Lewis*. This tenuous connection with the surface world is a pleasant diversion. Why, I don't know. We were now far beyond the reach of assistance.

I turned to my graphs. They were based on many hours of calculations and extrapolations especially from the previous 18,150-foot and 23,000-foot dives. My plan was to plummet the first 26,000 feet at a fast 3 feet per second. Then, I would reduce speed to 2 feet per second and finally to 1 foot per second until we detected the bottom on our 600-foot range echo sounder. This, I knew, would give me time to discharge sufficient ballast to break our speed for landing.

I recalled a very real hazard. The charts had warned me that the bottom of the cleft into which we were plunging was a scant one mile in width. Oceanographers have little knowledge of the velocity of the abyssal drift. It was easily possible that we might collide with a wall of the trench—a chilling thought! I had to be extremely cautious.

. . . 0920, depth 2,400 feet. Outside, total blackness. We dimmed our cabin light leaving only sufficient illumination to read our instruments. We wanted to dark-adapt our eyes for observation. We had entered the abyssal zone—the timeless world of eternal darkness. The water temperature had dropped abruptly when we had broken through the thermoclines. The chill was now penetrating the sphere. Both Walsh and I had been thoroughly soaked while preparing for the dive. Now it was time to change into dry clothing—no simple task in the restricted space of our cell—three feet across between the instruments and less than six feet high.

We broke out our first chocolate bars—the only food aboard. Walsh and I had a private joke about these "lunches." On the last dive I had provided lunch—Swiss Nestlé bars. This time Walsh offered to bring the lunch. He did—fifteen American Hershey bars.

. . . 0929–4,200 feet. A dribble of water entered around one of the cable lead-throughs. The small trickle meandered down the wall of the sphere into the bilge. This lead-through had always been perfectly sealed before.

. . . 0937–5,750 feet. A call from the *Wandank* on the UQC. The transmission was loud and clear. I was anxious to speak to Buono. It was important to know if the topside operation had gone off successfully. His musical Neapolitan voice came down to me through more than a mile of sea. "*Tutto bene, signor*" ["All is well, sir."], Buono assured me. Yes, he had had time to secure the hatch to the sas. All was in order topside. There was no cause for worry. It was raining and squally on the surface. If anything, the weather was deteriorating. I signed off, feeling completely detached from nature's vicissitudes in the world of the sun.

Now, as before, we were dropping down, down, down, at 200 feet per minute. I noted with relief that the first leak had stopped. Another now started. But this was an old friend from the previous dive. It started at around 18,000 feet and then sealed itself. It did, once again. The wax used in the watertight lead-throughs was apparently a little too old, so that it did not flow easily into some small crevices.

We continued to plunge. Black water rushed upward past us. Successively we overpassed the record depths that we had reached on preceding weeks. At 20,000 feet we were at the maximum depth of the normal Pacific sea floor. We were dropping into the open maw of the Mariana Trench, leaving the abyssal zone of the ocean and entering the hadal regions. Few bathyscaphes of the future need be designed for any depth greater than 20,000 feet. Only in trenches do we find the hadal depths. They comprise a mere 1 per cent of the ocean bottom.

Twenty-three thousand feet. This was a moment of special significance. The *Trieste*, Walsh, and I plummeted past the level of Dive 64. For the first time, man was descending so deep. For the fourth time the *Trieste* was carrying me into virgin depths, once in 1953, once in 1959, and now twice in 1960.

. . . 1124. The *Wandank* is talking to the *Lewis* on UQC. Then a call, barely audible, came through the still sea to us. By prearrangement, known to Walsh but unknown to me, we were to key tones on the UQC once out of voice range. An even number of tones meant good news; odd numbers indicated bad news. They had arranged a distress MAYDAY signal of five tones! Walsh transmitted a double signal, meaning "All's well."

. . . 1130–27,000 feet, right on schedule. Already I had dropped 6 tons of ballast to keep our speed of descent from building up beyond 3 feet per second. It was time to further reduce our velocity, anticipating the approaching bottom.

. . . 1144–29,150 feet. Now we were as deep under the sea as Mt. Everest is high above it. In the light cone, the water was crystal clear; no "sea snow" and not the slightest trace of plankton. This was a vast emptiness beyond all comprehension. There was, perhaps, a mile of water still beneath us, but the possibility of collision with the trench wall was still on my mind. I pushed the ballast button, slowing us down to two feet per second; then, to one foot per second, as decided before the dive.

. . . 1200–31,000 feet. I flipped on the echo sounder and sought for an echo to record on its 600-foot scale. No echo returned; the bottom, presumably, was still beyond 100 fathoms. Trying moments were ahead. We were venturing beyond the tested capabilities of the *Trieste*. On paper she could descend safely to ten miles and the sphere alone much more. I had confidence in those calculations. She was a complex of nuts and bolts, metal, plastic, and wire. But a dead thing? No. To me she was a living creature with a will to resist the seizing pressure. Above me, in the float, icy water was streaming in as the gasoline contracted, making the craft ever heavier and heavier. It was as if this icy water were coursing through my own veins.

The UQC was quiet now. The slow, silent descent was disturbed only by the hiss of oxygen escaping and the background hum of electronic instruments. I peered out the window, looking for bottom—and then back to the echo sounder. But there is only water and more water. Perhaps the sounder wasn't working. On the last dive we were 120 feet from the bottom before we picked it up. But now I could see noise recording. It made a long smudge on the graph from the iron ballast just released from the tub. "*Très bien*, it is working fine."

Then, an uneasy thought. What would the bottom be like? Clearly, we were in the axis of the trench and most probably we would miss the rocky walls. Dietz, who was aboard the *Lewis*, had advised me that there was an outside chance that the bottom sediment would be a flocculent and unconsolidated "soup" of recently deposited turbidity current beds. Could we sink and disappear into this material before being aware that we had contacted the bottom? Russian scientists aboard the *Vityaz* reportedly had tried many times, unsuccessfully, to lower a camera and snap pictures in trenches. But each time blank negatives came up. It appeared that the camera had entered a thick, soupy bottom before finally being triggered.

On the other hand, Dietz had emphasized, the H.M.S. *Challenger*, in 1951, had recovered a bottom sample not far distant from our diving site. It was diatomaceous ooze, composed almost entirely of siliceous remains of tropical diatom *Ethmodiscus rex*. These diatoms live in the surface water and their dead husks settle to the bottom. This would provide a firm bottom for landing. I could only hope that we would land on *Challenger* bottom.

. . . 1206—32,400 feet. A strong, muffled explosion! The sphere shook as though in a small earthquake. I caught Walsh's eye; he was watching me anxiously but calmly. "Have we touched bottom?" Walsh asked. "I do not believe so," I replied. We waited for something to happen. Nothing did. I wondered if the light case over the forward port had imploded. I tried to switch it on and it didn't light up. This could be the trouble but I wasn't satisfied. The noise we heard wasn't the high-pitched pop that had accompanied previous implosions. I studied the dials and switched off the UQC to silence the sphere. Still nothing happened. Our equilibrium seemed unaffected—we were not, apparently, losing gas. Our descent continued exactly as before. Without formal discussion, we agreed to continue down.

Thirty-four thousand feet—no bottom . . . 35,000 feet, only water and more water . . . 36,000 feet, descending smoothly at 60 feet per minute. Now we were at the supposed depth of the Challenger Deep. Had we found a new hole or was our depth gauge in error? Then a wry thought—perhaps we'd missed the bottom!

. . . 1256, Walsh's eyes were glued to the echo sounder. I was watching alternately through the port and at the fathometer. Suddenly, we saw black echoes on the graph. "There it is, Jacques! It looks like we have found it!" Yes, we had finally found it, just 42 fathoms down.

While I peered through the port preparing to touchdown, Walsh called off the soundings. "Thirty-six fathoms, echo coming in weakly—32—28—25—24—now we are getting a nice trace. Twenty-two fathoms—still going down—yes, this is it! Twenty—18—15—10—makes a nice trace now. Going right down. Six fathoms—we're slowing up, very slowly, we may come to a stop. You say you saw a small animal, possibly a red shrimp about one inch long? Wonderful, wonderful! Three fathoms—you can see the bottom through the port? Good—we've made it!"

The bottom appeared light and clear, a waste of snuff-colored ooze. We were landing on a nice, flat bottom of firm diatomaceous ooze. Indifferent to the nearly 200,000 tons of pressure clamped on her metal sphere, the *Trieste* balanced herself delicately on the few pounds of guide rope that lay on the bottom, making token claim, in the name of science and humanity, to the ultimate depths in all our oceans—the Challenger Deep.

The depth gauge read 6,300 fathoms—37,800 feet. The time—1306 hours.

The depth gauge was originally calibrated in Switzerland for pressures in fresh water, considering water a noncompressible fluid as is usual in these cases. After the dive, the gauge was recalibrated by the Naval Weapons Plant in Washington, D.C. Then several oceanographers (especially Dr. John Knauss of Scripps Institution of Oceanography and Dr. John Lyman of the National Science Foundation) applied corrections for salinity, compressibility, temperature, and gravity. Agreement was reached that the depth attained was 35,800 feet—or 5,966 fathoms. This computed depth agrees well with the deepest sonic soundings obtained by American, British, and Russian oceanographic ships, all of which had reported the round-trip sounding time in the Challenger Deep at almost precisely fourteen seconds. The corrected figure confirmed that the *Trieste* had indeed attained the *deepest* hole in the trench.

And as we were settling this final fathom, I saw a wonderful thing. Lying on the bottom just beneath us was some type of flatfish, resembling a sole, about one foot long and six inches across. Even as I saw him, his two round eyes on top of his head spied us—a monster of steel—invading his silent realm. Eyes? Why should he have eyes? Merely to see phosphorescence? The floodlight that bathed him was the first real light ever to enter his hadal realm. Here, in an instant, was the answer that biologists had asked for decades. Could life exist in the greatest depths of the ocean? It could! And not only that, here, apparently, was a true, bony teleost fish, not a primitive ray or elasmobranch. Yes, a highly evolved vertebrate, in time's arrow very close to man himself.

Slowly, extremely slowly, this flatfish swam away. Moving along the bottom, partly in the ooze and partly in the water, he disappeared into his night. Slowly too—perhaps everything is slow at the bottom of the sea—Walsh and I shook hands.

Walsh keyed the UQC four times, the prearranged signal for "on the bottom." We assumed that we were far beyond the range of voice communication. Simply as a matter of routine and perhaps to enjoy the companionship of his own voice, Walsh called on the voice circuit. "*Wandank, Wandank*. This is the *Trieste*. We are at the bottom of the Challenger Deep at sixty-three hundred fathoms. Over."

To our complete astonishment a voice from nowhere drifted through to us. "*Trieste, Trieste*, this is *Wandank*. I hear you faint but clear. Will you repeat your depth? Over."

Walsh repeated the depth and added, "Our ETA on the surface is seventeen hundred hours. Over."

The voice came back to us charged with excitement, "*Trieste*, this is *Wandank*. Understand. Six three zero zero fathoms. Roger. Out."

Heartened by our voice link with friends above, we set about quickly to make our scientific observations. The temperature of the water was an icy 2.4° C (36.5 F). It had warmed gradually and continually from the lowest reading of 1.4° C at about 2,000 fathoms.

Next, I peered intently through the port. I sought visual evidence of bottom current. The depths of the Mediterranean are usually still, but I had become accustomed to strong bottom currents off San Diego. The water here appeared still; at least, below any threshold I could detect. Of course I knew it could not be completely stagnant. This life on the bottom was ample proof of some interchange of water. Water interchange is a prerequisite for oxygen replenishment, which, in turn, is a prerequisite for life.

As the turbidity that we had stirred up in landing

began to clear, I saw a beautiful red shrimp. The ivory ooze was almost flat. There were none of the small mounds and burrows such as those so common in the Mediterranean. Nor was there the usual churning of the sea floor by the bottom-living animals. No animal tracks could be seen anywhere. The bottom was not perfectly smooth, however. I noted some minor undulations suggestive of animal plowings.

For twenty minutes we made our scientific observations. The vertical current meter had been destroyed during the tow; the horizontal meter was undamaged but it gave a reading of zero. I exposed some film to check on radiation from radioactive sources. (When later developed, the results were negative.) Then I switched on the aft searchlight for Walsh who peered out. Suddenly he called out, "I see now what caused the shock at thirty thousand feet!"

He pointed to the large plastic window that permits us to see through the antechamber to the sea beyond. The plastic window was fissured with small open horizontal cracks. It had failed because of the differential contraction between the metal of the sas and the plastic. Fortunately, it was still in place. It presented no immediate threat to our safety. But I realized at once that it could mean some real trouble later on.

Once we surface, that antechamber is our only escape way. Before we could get out of the sphere all of the water must be blown from the sas by compressed air. If the plastic window didn't remain watertight we would be in a desperate predicament. True, we always carried a metal coverplate on the tug to seal off the window against this eventuality. But under the present sea conditions, it would be next to impossible to send divers down to attempt to install it. The numerous white-tipped sharks in the area would be an added obstacle. If the sas could not be cleared, the alternative wasn't happy: We would have to be towed back to Guam, sealed in our cell, to be finally extracted upon arrival. In the event of head seas, this could be a five-day ordeal. Flooding the sphere or escaping by aqualung was another possibility but this would be very difficult. (Let me say here that a new mode of construction, very simple indeed, will make it possible to definitely avoid a similar accident in the future.)

Our original plan was to remain on the sea floor for thirty minutes. This plan we hastily revised. As it stood, our ETA of 1700 hours gave us only a scant daylight margin of ninety minutes to effect any necessary emergency measures. There was no time to lose. At 1326, I cut the current on the electromagnet for thirty-six seconds, releasing 800 pounds of ballast. Slowly, the *Trieste* lifted her massive 150-ton hulk off the bottom. The long seven-mile return trip to the world of man began.

We were both chilled. The temperature in the sphere had dropped to 50° F. Our feet were especially cold. In our confined space there was no way to exercise and increase the circulation of blood. I knew that the canisters for absorbing carbon dioxide gave off good heat. We each shoved one of the hot canisters under our sweaters to serve as hot-water bottles.

It was about then that, through the port, we noticed the bright flecks of paint that were caught in the burble of our wake. It was not unusual to see a few flecks in deep dives, for at great depths, the sphere is actually shrunk under pressure and some paint is bound to be loosened. But this was more than I usually noted before.

As we ascended, the gasoline in the float expanded, forcing out the salt water. Relieved of her load, the *Trieste* ascended ever faster. Our rate of speed increased from a little more than 1 foot per second to a rocketing 3 feet per second at 4,000 fathoms. More exactly, our speed of ascent was 1.5 feet per second at the beginning, then 2.5 feet per second at 30,000 feet, 3 feet per second at 20,000 feet, 4 feet per second at 10,000 feet, and finally 5 feet per second at about 3,000 feet. The bathyscaphe was working perfectly, no oscillation, vibration, or flutter.

I was keeping a careful watch on the gasoline temperature gauge—and for good reason. Like any fluid, gasoline heats as it compresses and cools as it expands. My calculations and extrapolations from earlier dives indicated that the gasoline temperature could fall well below freezing during the ascent if we remained on bottom long enough for the gasoline to cool to the surrounding sea water temperature (36.5° F). During the descent, the chill of the deep water had more than offset the compressional heating. The gasoline had dropped from its surface temperature of 84° F to 60° F on the bottom.

Our brief stay on the bottom of only twenty minutes was a favorable factor. The gasoline did not have time to cool down to the water temperature. That gave us added buoyancy, saving a ton or two of ballast needed for lifting us off the bottom. But now, as we rose, the gasoline temperature dropped rapidly.

I was not worried about the gasoline freezing, of course. The danger was that the water pipes passing through the gasoline might be frozen by the subfreezing gasoline. We had lagged the pipes against this eventuality, as well as carefully calculating their diameter in the beginning. If these water lines froze, the fragile float of the bathyscaphe would explode as easily as a child's balloon.

Constantly, during the three and a half hour ascent, Walsh tried to make contact with the surface ships. We were anxious to tell them about our problem with the cracked window and prepare them for a possible emergency. No luck.

. . . 1602–depth 13,000 feet. Walsh heard the pinging of the *Lewis*'s sonar. A few moments later he heard the *Wandank* on the UQC. They were trying desperately to contact us and confirm our ETA. We just could not make a two-way contact.

The sphere rose ever up and up, reversing the diurnal rhythm of her descent. We were borne upward from night into gray predawn. Faster and faster we rushed toward the light of day. I noted at 1617 hours, that the temperature gauge for the gasoline read 32° F. When we arrived on the surface, the gasoline temperature was 10° F below freezing. The piping had not caused us any trouble.

As we approached the surface, our rocketing speed attained five feet per second. But the *Trieste* was still stable with no sign of oscillation or fluttering. Once we had pierced the thermocline, the warmer surface water decelerated us slightly. The lighter water increased the apparent weight of the bathyscaphe by about one ton.

At 1656—almost exactly on our ETA—the *Trieste* broke the surface. The rocking of the sphere told us we had returned to the heaving breast of the sea. Our seven-mile elevator ride was ended.

In a matter of moments we would know the worst. We had conserved our meager supply of chocolate bars against the real possibility that we would be trapped in our sphere for several days. I decided to bleed air into the sas extremely slowly so that as little pressure as possible would press against the cracked window. In the daylight I could see that the plastic window had expanded again, closing up any fissures. Walsh slowly, very slowly, fed three bottles of compressed air into the sas. I watched, tensely, through the port controlling the bleeding of the air. Finally, the water level dropped below the level of the window in the door. A dense fog appeared in the antechamber produced by the sudden release of pressure. The sas was cleared!

We wasted little time pushing open the door to our vault. We clambered up the sas, through the hatch, and finally topside to the sunshine and steaming tropic heat. Two Navy jets zoomed in out of nowhere. They screamed over our heads, dipping their wings in salute; an Air Force rescue plane followed. The *Lewis* had already found us and was lying á few hundred yards off. Off in the distance, the *Wandank* was bearing down upon us.

Aboard the *Lewis*, John Pflaum, the Nekton photographer, spotted the vivid fluorescent stripes on the conning tower in the expanse of whitecaps, the very instant we breached the surface, four miles off the destroyer escort's bow. He shouted: "There she is! Right on her ETA!" The cry, "There she is! There she is!" was taken up as the *Lewis* raced to the scene. Normally, the bathyscaphe crew appears topside in a matter of minutes. When we didn't appear at once, there were some minutes of great apprehension aboard the *Lewis*. Was the sphere flooded? Had the *Trieste* delivered two dead bodies to the surface? No! It was nearly fifteen minutes before Walsh and I appeared on deck to relieve the deep uneasiness because we emptied the sas very slowly.

Coming toward us, battling punishing seas, was the small rubber raft. It was manned by two sailors. With them were two photographers brandishing cameras. We were indeed back to civilization! The photographers were shouting. They were pleading with us to wave; to make some appropriate gesture. We complied, not for the papers, not for posterity. We waved, gratefully, to the world of sunshine.

After we returned to Guam, the Navy dispatched a special plane which flew us back to the United States. A few days later, the importance of our achievement was officially proclaimed in Washington, where President Eisenhower personally presented awards. And shortly after the presentation at the White House, I received the following letter:

DEAR MR. PICCARD:

It was a distinct pleasure for me to have the opportunity to present to you an award last Thursday for an outstanding contribution to the United States and science in the field of oceanographic research. . . .

. . . As a citizen of Switzerland, a country admired by all the free world for its love of freedom and independence, you have the gratitude of all of the people of the United States for helping to further open the doors of this important scientific field.

With all good wishes for your continued success,

Sincerely,

DWIGHT EISENHOWER

FEBRUARY 9, 1960

Part 2

Fighting, Working, Salvaging

The Secret Naval Disaster

by
David Masters

We have seen how profoundly the design and equipment of the submarine have changed since the Revolutionary War. But while the shell which encloses them has grown in size and power, the submariners themselves remain the same—a valiant breed, prepared to face the perils of the sea and enemy action with steady nerves. The deeds of the submariners fill some of the most thrilling and at times horrifying pages in the literature of war, and have had a profound effect on the destinies of nations. It was the sinking of the Lusitania by a German submarine that precipitated the entry of the United States into World War I, thus sealing the doom of Kaiser Wilhelm. The submarine blockades of Britain in both world wars almost brought that intrepid nation to its knees. The exploits of American sub-

mariners against the Japanese in the Pacific encompassed everything from the destruction of aircraft carriers and battleships to the tragic "sunk without trace." From the vast literature dealing with submariners we have selected the following episode for the uniqueness of its subject matter, for the manner in which it combines warfare and salvage, and for the interest and excitement of its narrative.

INSTEAD of a gentle tap on the door to herald a morning cup of tea, the sleeping people on the harbor front at Gibraltar were wakened at six o'clock in the morning by the sound of a big explosion, followed by another and another. The sentries on the Rock and the sailors on watch saw the tanker *Denbydale* sink with a broken back while the merchantman *Durham*, a fine cargo ship of 10,000 tons, and the *Fiona Shell*, a storage tanker, slowly foundered. That morning of September 19, 1941, the Italian Navy proved that it could still strike hard in spite of its losses at Taranto and Matapan. It was Prince Giulio Valerio Borghese, a descendant of an ancient Sienese family which has played a large part in Italian history, who carried the three human torpedoes, each ridden by two men, that were launched from the deck of the submarine *Scire* to run the gantlet of the Gibraltar defenses and make that daring attack.

A month earlier the enemy had made their first attempt on the shipping in Gibraltar Harbor with two other human torpedoes, but the electric batteries on which they ran had flickered out and frustrated the attempt. The second time they succeeded. Escaping ashore, the six Italians induced the Spanish authorities to turn a blind eye and allow them to return to Italy.

Men with long memories recalled that an earlier generation of Italian seamen had ridden astride torpedoes to attack the Austrian fleet in the harbor of Dalmatia during the 1914–1918 war. Now a second generation was showing the same spirit.

The repercussions of the explosions in Gibraltar Bay penetrated to the other end of the Mediterranean where the famous battleship *Queen Elizabeth* and her consort *Valiant* were moored in Alexandria Harbor. The fleet air arm's attack on the Italian fleet in Taranto Harbor on November 11, 1940, with the torpedoing of three battleships as well as other damage, and Admiral Cunningham's victory at Matapan on March 24, 1941, which led to the destruction of three Italian cruisers and the immobilization of the rest of the Italian Navy, gave the Royal Navy the surface supremacy of the Mediterranean. But Admiral Cunningham was too wise to underrate the enemy. This attack on Gibraltar made it plain that though the Italian naval authorities were chary of risking their remaining ships, Italian seamen were still glad to risk their lives for their country.

More than willing to take chances that promised decisive results, as in the Battle of Matapan, Admiral Cunningham was taking no risks with the *Queen*

Elizabeth and the *Valiant* while they were in harbor. To make doubly sure that the anchorage was safe, a special check was made on the defenses of Alexandria Harbor.

While the Italians were concentrating their attacks on Gibraltar, using the interned merchantman *Fulgar* in Cadiz Bay as a secret base for their frogmen and two-man torpedoes, they were quietly planning to strike at the precious British battleships in Alexandria Harbor. In their initial effort the submarine carrying the attackers was surprised on the surface and wiped out with all on board. A second attempt was launched on the morning of December 14, 1941, when Prince Borghese glided away from the island of Lero in the Dodecanese in the *Scire* with three two-man torpedoes housed in big cylinders on the deck of the submarine and six operators as passengers, as well as two reserve crews in case they were needed. These specialists were clever swimmers whose training had been long and arduous.

They had worked as teams to find out the idiosyncrasies of their craft, practicing their code of underwater signals by touch until their reactions were automatic. They were well drilled in taking their craft up and down or ahead and astern, stopping her as desired to detach her 600-pound nose of high explosive and attach it to the bottom of a ship.

The specialists in this branch of the Italian Navy nicknamed their torpedoes "pigs," while in the Royal Navy they were known as "chariots," and as chariots we shall refer to them hereafter. The Italian chariot was shaped like a torpedo which was 21 feet long and 3 feet in diameter. It had a propeller astern and two bucket seats let into the hull on which the men sat astride wearing light watertight suits and breathing masks, with an oxygen container on their backs which enabled them to breathe under water for considerable periods. The torpedo was packed with intricate machinery and propelled by batteries which gave it a range of twelve miles, while it was equipped with tanks that could be flooded or blown for diving or surfacing. Its maximum diving depth was 100 feet, and in making an attack it was stopped on the bottom as near as possible to the ship to allow the mechanic to dismount and help his companion to detach the warhead and sling it under the bottom of the ship by attaching clips to the bilge keel.

Lero was about 430 miles from Alexandria in a straight line. But it was by no means a straight course that the *Scire* was able to follow, for there were British minefields specially laid to trap marauding enemy submarines and Prince Borghese had to navigate the *Scire* with circumspection to avoid them. Submerging by day to keep out of sight, he made what progress he could on the surface at night. He was determined not to be caught and destroyed like the first submarine.

The attacking teams were well briefed. Italian reconnaissance aircraft had reported that two battleships of the *Queen Elizabeth* class and an aircraft carrier as well as cruisers and other ships were lying snugly at anchor in Alexandria Harbor. The attackers had studied the silhouettes of the British battleships until they could recognize them in the dark, which was exactly what they would have to do. If the tragic end of the first attempt obtruded occasionally into their thoughts, they probably found some solace in the fact that many of the Gibraltar attackers had managed to escape through Spain, and their own chances of getting away were at least as good. Their plan of escape was to swim ashore after carrying out their mission and make their way in the guise of French seamen to Rosetta where another submarine would wait on the nights of December 24 and 26 to pick them up at a fixed rendezvous. Lieutenant de la Penne was detailed to attack one battleship, the *Valiant*, Captain Marceglia was to attack the other battleship, the *Queen Elizabeth*, and Captain Martellotta was to deal with the aircraft carrier.

Just before nine o'clock on the night of December 18 the *Scire* nosed her way into position a mile or so north of Alexandria Harbor. Prince Borghese brought her gently up until her conning tower was just out of the water while her decks were awash. The attackers climbed out of the conning tower and after considerable difficulty managed to pull their chariots from the protecting cylinders. They took their seats and waited as the *Scire* gradually submerged. The launching of the chariots went without a hitch. They were safely afloat.

The sea was flat calm as Lieutenant de la Penne

took a look around to get his bearings. The conditions for their attack were as perfect as they could wish for. It was so dark that nothing was visible. Fixing his course, the leader set off with his tiny flotilla towards the harbor entrance. The men were submerged up to the neck, ready to drop under in a moment to avoid being seen. They glided along quietly at about two miles an hour and made such progress that their leader was afraid of arriving before the time scheduled, so they halted awhile to eat some of their rations before they went in to the attack.

They were moving along parallel to the breakwater some distance from the shore when they received a nasty jolt. A motor launch without lights began to speed up and down outside the entrance to the harbor throwing depth charges from time to time to kill any submarine that happened to be lurking thereabouts. They did not like it at all. They sat there with the sea up to their necks, watching the launch that menaced their lives.

But luck was with them. After a while the buoys marking the channel into the harbor lit up. They knew it portended a ship entering or leaving the harbor. Then the lights on the boom itself shone out in the darkness to indicate that the boom across the entrance was to be opened to give passage to a ship.

Here was a heaven-sent opportunity which de la Penne seized avidly. Giving the other crews instructions to dodge into the harbor while the boom was open for the ship, he lurked with them at the harbor mouth awaiting a chance to slip through. Suddenly a destroyer loomed up out of the blackness with another following at a safe interval. The three chariots, going ahead for all they were worth, made for the entrance and managed to steal in undetected in the wake of the warships. It was a perilous passage. The wash flung them about and bumped them against the boom. More than once they were almost capsized by the swell and had difficulty in righting their craft; but they got through safely, the boom closed behind them and the lighted buoys went out, leaving them in absolute darkness to separate and find their way to their targets.

As de la Penne crept into the harbor he detected two cruisers at anchor and recognized the silhouette of the interned French battleship *Lorraine* before he made out the British battleship that was his target. Moving stealthily toward her, he suddenly hit a steel protection net some 50 or 60 yards away from the hull. It was unexpected. He nosed around, seeking a gap like a terrier looking for a rat hole. Taking the chariot down, he hoped to find a way under, but the net touched bottom and he could not get through. His suit was letting in water. He began to feel very cold and wondered how much longer he would be able to carry on.

Surfacing again, he took the risk of manipulating the chariot over the top of the net, fearing all the time that the guns would open up. But he remained unseen, so he moved forward a few yards and then submerged to bring the chariot up to the battleship.

To his chagrin, the chariot stopped dead. A wire had fouled the propeller. Giving his companion Bianci instructions to clear the obstruction, he waited for him to do so. When he went to see if the propeller were freed, he could find no trace of his teammate. Bianci had vanished. Swimming around under the water, de la Penne strove to find the lost mechanic. He was not there. Striking upward to the surface, he swam quietly about seeking him, but Bianci had disappeared.

Wet and cold and rather shaken, he dived again to his chariot and fought to unwind the wire rope which was twisted round the propeller. He struggled and wrenched and strained at it, but it was twisted so tightly that he failed to untangle it.

Being only 50 or 60 feet away from the battleship, he relinquished his efforts to free the propeller and determined to try to move the warhead to the battleship single-handed. It was a tremendous task that would have been hopeless had the warhead not been slightly buoyant.

The leak in his suit became worse as he dragged the charge slowly along the muddy bottom towards the ship. His exertions were tiring him. His goggles became so misty with sweat that he could not see what he was about. Trying to clear them, he accidentally let in a little water and was forced to gulp it down to get rid of it. Rising to the surface to make sure that he had dragged the charge right under the battleship, he went down again to set the time fuse. The task of clipping the charge to the bilge keel was beyond his strength, so he left it lying on the bottom.

Utterly exhausted, he rose to the surface. Tearing the diving gear from his head and back, he started to swim slowly away from the *Valiant*. At once a sentry located the swimmer with an Aldis lamp and raised the alarm. Searchlights flashed out. Machine guns began to chatter. Turning under the bow of the warship, the tired Italian clambered up on a buoy where, to his amazement, he found the missing Bianci.

Losing consciousness in trying to free the propeller, Bianci had floated to the surface, where he came to and took refuge on the buoy.

By now the harbor was alive with searchlights. Angry voices shouted from the deck of the battleship as one of the Italians tried to climb a cable. A shot drove him down again and in a few minutes a launch arrived to take the two prisoners to the battleship.

They disclosed that they were Italians, removed their diving suits, and handed over their identification papers. News of the capture was passed at once to the *Queen Elizabeth* with a request for an interpreter. Plying the prisoners with questions, the interpreter did his best to get some information from them, but he failed. Then the prisoners were rushed ashore to the Ras-el-Tin naval barracks for another interrogation. This time they were questioned separately by the

Chief Intelligence Officer, but not a word would they say about where the charge was placed. Again and again they were pressed to speak, but they steadfastly refused to give anything away.

The presence of the prisoners was proof that dire peril threatened. They were accordingly rushed back to the *Valiant* where her commander, Captain Charles Morgan, again strove to learn the truth from them. They would not speak.

Carrying out the instructions of the Chief Intelligence Officer, Captain Morgan motioned to the Italian officer and told the interpreter to explain that he would be involved in anything that happened to the ship. The prisoner remained silent.

"Take him below," said Captain Morgan.

The prisoner was thereupon escorted to a small compartment deep in the bowels of the ship right over the spot where he had placed the charge. Giving him a glass of rum to warm him up after his long immersion, the British naval officer locked the door on him, leaving him to face the risk of being blown up by his own explosion or of disclosing where the charge was laid.

Meanwhile Engineer Captain Marceglia had managed to identify the silhouette of the battleship that was marked as his quarry. Proceeding quietly toward his target, he bumped into the defense net exactly as de la Penne had done and found that he could not go on. Those defense nets had been placed in position by the special order of Admiral Cunningham only the previous day. It looked as though the British Intelligence service had gained an inkling of what was afoot.

Backing away from the net, Marceglia began to hunt for a way in. Slowly he moved around the barrier, examining it carefully to find a place where he could get through. The net was far too heavy to lift at the bottom to allow him to squeeze underneath. Eventually after scouting around he found a small space that was just big enough to allow the chariot to enter.

No sound came from the *Queen Elizabeth.* Approaching quietly, he took the chariot to the bottom and moved forward until he seemed to be right under the ship. Determined not to make a mistake, he rose to the surface to ensure that he was in the right position, then dived again and began to help his teammate Schergat attach the charge to the bilge keel by the clips. The mechanic, who had been breathing oxygen for some time, began to suffer the ill-effects. Shaken by severe spasms and feeling very sick, owing to the excess of oxygen, he was forced to abandon his efforts and rest awhile. Marceglia carried on without hesitation and succeeded in attaching the charge and fixing the fuse.

As quietly as they had entered, they stole out of the harbor and made for the beach at Macello, which was very isolated and quiet. They then destroyed all their equipment and wandered ashore to pose as harmless Frenchmen.

Despite the care with which everything had been worked out, the Italian planners made one mistake.

They furnished the charioteers with English money which the Egyptians would not accept. The Italians were therefore landed in an enemy country without money or means of sustenance. However, they played their parts astonishingly well all day and after several narrow escapes they made their way to Rosetta.

Their freedom was short-lived. A suspicious Egyptian policeman challenged them on the evening of December 20 and, taking them to Alexandria, handed them over to the British naval authorities.

Captain Martellotta, on the third chariot, was in rather a quandary when he came to look for the aircraft carrier. In spite of a careful search, he failed to locate her. She had in fact already departed from Alexandria. Concluding that she had gone, he began to look for another worthwhile target. At first he decided to attack a warship which he thought was a battleship, but recognizing her as a cruiser he drew away. Finally he came on a tanker, which he planned to destroy and thereby turn the harbor into a blazing inferno. He aimed to blow up the tanker so that her oil would float out over the surface and then set this oil alight with floating incendiary bombs.

At the critical moment, just as he maneuvered the chariot under the tanker, he, too, fell ill owing to an excess of oxygen. Swimming to the surface, he took off his mask to fill his lungs with fresh air. While he was recovering, his mechanic Marino succeeded in fixing the charge unaided and set the fuse. He then steered the chariot to the surface, where Martellotta remounted, and they glided away from the tanker and put down four floating incendiary bombs about a hundred yards from the tanker. Jettisoning their equipment, they swam ashore, to enjoy no more than an hour or two of freedom before an Egyptian policeman captured them and handed them to the British authorities.

While these events were happening, de la Penne was immured in the bowels of the *Valiant*. Bianci in another compartment was so worn out with experiences that he fell fast asleep.

For nearly an hour de la Penne suffered the ordeal, looking anxiously at his watch, wondering if the charge would go off before time or if it would fail. Just before 6 A.M. he could stand the suspense no longer. He hammered on the door and shouted that he wanted to speak to the captain. The master-at-arms ran into the wardroom to tell the captain.

"Bring him up," ordered Captain Morgan.

In a few moments de la Penne appeared before him. "There will soon be an explosion," said the prisoner to the interpreter.

"Where have you put the charge?" the captain demanded.

The prisoner refused to answer.

At that moment came the sound of an explosion from the tanker some distance away. "Is that the explosion?" the captain demanded, through the interpreter.

The prisoner hunched his shoulders.

"Will the *Valiant* be concerned?" they demanded, but de la Penne would give no information.

"Take him down again," ordered the captain.

By now a line had been passed right under the keel of the ship from stem to stern to dislodge any charge that might have been fixed there. As the charge was lying on the sea bed, it was not swept clear. All the watertight doors were closed and the entire crew drawn up on the upper deck where they were told what had happened.

At 6:05 A.M. the *Valiant* heaved under the shock of the explosion. A cataract of water shot up into the heavens and rained down on them as the battleship settled down on the mud.

Lieutenant de la Penne thought the end had come. The floor moved up under his feet, fittings fell about him, the place was filled with acrid smoke. By a miracle he was unharmed except for a slight bruise on the leg. Opening a scuttle, he strove to climb out, but the aperture was too small. Then he tried the entrance. The door opened at his touch and he made his way to the upper deck.

A quarter of a mile away the *Queen Elizabeth* lay at anchor. Even as he gazed across at her in the morning light a great explosion shook her and she, too, settled down in the mud five minutes after the *Valiant*.

Thus two of the finest British battleships were sunk. It was a stunning disaster for the Royal Navy. Its strength had been sadly sapped in evacuating the troops from Greece and Crete. The *Barham* had already been torpedoed with a heavy death roll. The *Warspite* had been knocked out by a bomb which dropped straight down the funnel and ruined the machinery. Now this tragic loss made the Italians masters of the Mediterranean. They could go anywhere they liked and do anything they wanted. Great Britain had not a single battleship in the Mediterranean.

That incredible luck which enabled six men to sink two battleships and a tanker in Alexandria Harbor without the loss of a single life deserted the enemy at the crucial moment. Early on that morning of December 19 Prince Borghese surfaced in the *Scire* off Alexandria and watched anxiously for signs of explosions that would tell him whether the great plan had succeeded. Time passed. Nothing happened. At last unable to risk his ship on the surface any longer, he was compelled to dive and speed away before the explosions occurred.

Five days later, on Christmas Eve, the submarine waited at the rendezvous off Rosetta, scanning the sea and shore in vain for the men who did not come. Returning to the rendezvous on December 26, he watched tensely for the signals that would tell him all was well. There were no signals, no trace of his compatriots, so he was forced to go back without the slightest knowledge of what had happened.

The Italians had achieved one of the most remarkable victories in naval warfare, but they did not know it. That the British were able to keep it dark was as extraordinary as the Italian victory itself. Thousands of British seamen on the sunken battleships knew what had occurred. Axis spies abounded in Cairo and Alexandria. It was phenomenal that nothing leaked out to the enemy. The mass silence of the British sailors was a fine tribute to their discipline and a finer tribute to their patriotism.

The enemy was naturally on tenterhooks to learn the result of the attack. Italian aircraft reconnoitered Alexandria Harbor. Everything looked the same as before. There were no overturned ships, no signs of wreckage. The *Queen Elizabeth* and the *Valiant* rode serenely at their anchors. They were apparently undamaged. The fact that they had sunk and were sitting upright on the bottom was not visible from the air, so the Italians were absolutely deceived and kept their warships safely in harbor instead of exploiting their incredible victory.

On that morning of December 19, 1941, the balance of power in the Mediterranean was dramatically changed. As long as the enemy could be bluffed into believing that British naval power was unaffected, the bitter penalties of disaster might yet be avoided.

Directly the two battleships settled on the mud, the naval command began to grapple with the two most urgent problems—to maintain secrecy and to refloat the ships. The sound of explosions in Alexandria was not unusual. Raiders often flew over to drop bombs, the guns were continually speaking. To casual eyes everything in the harbor seemed to be normal, yet behind the calm exterior all the human resources of the navy suddenly erupted into activity. The first essential was to discover the damage in order to see how it could be rectified.

Calling Commander G. J. Wheeler, Admiral Sir Andrew Cunningham indicated the steps he proposed to take to deal with the *Queen Elizabeth*, and asked for the salvage officer's opinion. The measures suggested would have brought the rescue ships clustering round the battleship like flies round a honeypot.

"Well, sir, they are bound to send a plane over to see what has happened. If they see her with a lot of craft round her they will know they have got her. I suggest that we first of all pump out the oil to bring her upright. If they see her with an oiler alongside there is nothing unusual in that and they will think she is all right," said the fleet salvage officer, and the admiral agreed.

Then the salvage officer got busy on the job, aided by every officer and man on the ships. Naval divers, inspecting the *Valiant*, reported a vast hole in the hull on the port side of the bow between the gun turrets. Without going too closely into details, suffice to say that the hole was large enough to park a bus and still leave room to spare. The flooding of the compartments pulled the bow down and greatly increased the draft forward, which made it necessary to remove as much weight as possible.

A tanker was soon brought alongside and the ship's pumps began to pump out oil. Salvage pumps were brought in to pump out damaged compartments where fractured bulkheads were sealed with pads and shored up. Luckily the light and power plants functioned normally and did all that was asked of them. A steady stream of oil gushed from the *Valiant* into the tanker while the salvage pumps sucked the water out of the bowels of the ship. Gradually her slight list was corrected and she came upright. Thousands of tons of water and oil were pumped out. Prudence, however, dictated that the water flooding the depth charges should remain undisturbed. Anchors, cables, shells, and charges were lifted out of the ship as fast as men could work.

Before midday on December 20, 1941, the *Valiant* was ready to float over the keel blocks in the dry dock with eight or nine inches to spare. But the salvage officer was not satisfied. Work continued for the rest of the day, removing ammunition and other things until the bow of the ship was raised another six or seven inches. Then at nine o'clock on the morning of December 21, just fifty-one hours after she was sunk, the *Valiant* was maneuvered safely into dry dock to be repaired. It was a magnificent feat, due, as the fleet salvage officer said, to the splendid cooperation of all the officers and men aboard.

Sitting on the mud with a slight list, the *Queen Elizabeth* was not so easy to deal with. Robbed of light and power by the explosion, she was wrapped in gloom until submarines could be brought up to supply these necessaries. Then the naval divers, working in the mud and feeling their way under the hull, were very baffled. That there must be a hole was obvious, otherwise the battleship would not be resting on the sea bed. Yet although they explored the bottom foot by foot for hour after hour they could not find it. Terribly handicapped by the ooze, they had to work by touch, for despite the care with which they moved they could not avoid fogging the water. On a clean, sandy bottom they could have seen perfectly by the light of the sun; but the mud on the bottom combined with the gloom caused by the overhang of the ship, which cut off the light, forced them to work blind.

All through the morning and afternoon the search for the damage was pursued. It was not until seven o'clock in the evening, thirteen hours after the explosion, that the divers were able to locate an opening in the ship's hull. It was more of a fissure than a hole, seven or eight feet long by a couple of inches wide. It puzzled the salvage officer how so small an opening could achieve such big results.

Next day the divers went down to continue their examination, but in their all-day search they failed to find the hole which they had examined overnight. This gives an idea of the difficulties under which they worked. Darkness had fallen before they came upon a clamp attached to the bilge of the ship. The line hanging from the clamp told them that the charge must have been fixed in the vicinity.

Meanwhile the pumps transferred hundreds of tons

of fuel oil from the *Queen Elizabeth* to the tanker. The men worked ceaselessly to remove the ammunition to lighten the ship. Flooded boiler rooms indicated that the damage was in that neighborhood, although the divers could not find it. Long experience had taught Commander Wheeler that there must be broken inlets which would cause a deal of trouble if they were overlooked, so he ordered plugs and pads to be prepared to seal them while the task of shoring up weakened bulkheads went on inside the ship.

Three days after the explosion the battleship was brought into an upright position. The large weight of oil and ammunition discharged had reduced her draft by eight or nine inches. It seemed little enough after all their efforts, yet to the salvage officer the gain was appreciable.

Even now the extent of the damage remained unknown. There was not the slightest sign on deck that anything had happened. Nothing was broken or displaced. It was an astonishing state of affairs that mystified the salvage officer. As a rule a ship's deck will give some indication of where the damage is situated below. But the upperworks of the *Queen Elizabeth* gave nothing away.

With the naval divers working until exhausted, it became obvious that more were required to cope with the work to be done, yet not another diver was available on the station. The decision was now made to use compressed air to drive the water from some of the flooded compartments to regain buoyancy. By the night of December 23 the bow of the *Queen Elizabeth* was raised another three or four inches.

On Christmas Eve a gale kept the divers from working until late in the afternoon, but when they went down at last they were able for the first time to gain something like a true idea of the damage. There was a hole under the boiler room that would have engulfed a couple of suburban houses. As the ship had been sitting on it, the divers were unable to find it until she began to rise. The divers spent Christmas Day checking and confirming the damage.

Now that the worst was known, the help of other divers became imperative. In this emergency Admiral Cunningham dispatched a request for divers to the Commander in Chief of the South Atlantic Fleet, Rear Admiral D. A. Burgen at Simonstown in South Africa, and on December 26, Lieutenant Keeble started to fly from Cairo to Cape Town in his quest for divers to salve the *Queen Elizabeth*.

The South African Minister of Railways came to the rescue with the offer of four divers, Priestly, Davidson, Shorrt, and Winter, who were on the staff of the railways. Satisfying himself that they were capable of doing the work required, Lieutenant Keeble asked them if they would volunteer for a special job which was very important and very secret.

"You will be away some weeks," he told them.

All agreed instantly. Knowing nothing, the only thing they could tell their families was not to expect them back too soon.

When they started out for Pretoria on January 17, 1942, their ultimate destination was a profound secret. Reaching Zwartkop on January 19, they embarked in an aircraft, still puzzling over their destination. Landing at last in Cairo they were rushed to Alexandria by car to meet Commander Wheeler, who explained what he wanted them to do.

The fleet salvage officer and his team had not been idle. They had wrestled to get recalcitrant salvage pumps to the spots where they could suck the water out of flooded compartments. They had heaved out the giant anchors and mighty cables. They had fitted connection after connection in readiness for the air compressors.

The work was never-ending, and all their toil seemed to make little change. Yet the difference, almost imperceptible, was eagerly marked by the salvage officer. His careful measurements showed that the bow was slowly swinging up, not much, it is true, half an inch, an inch, or two inches. Every ton taken out gave the battleship a little extra buoyancy. From 42 feet, which marked the draft at the bow after the explosion, the salvage squads had managed by December 28, 1941, to reduce it to 39 feet 2 inches.

Commander Wheeler was under no illusion. Before he could move the ship into dry dock he had to reduce her draft to something under 35 feet. He was six inches on the right side aft, but over 4 feet to the bad forward.

A diver on loan from the Suez Canal Company

sought to explore through the mighty hole in the double bottom of the ship. The jagged edges of torn and twisted plates made his movements hazardous. An air pipe caught and cut by the sharp spurs of metal, a tear in his diving suit, might have proved fatal. Moving warily in the blackness, he penetrated upward for 15 feet in an effort to find the boilers. Thwarted in his efforts to locate them, in spite of their immense size, he made his way down again and emerged safely.

That day of December 30, 1941, the compressed-air connections on which the salvage officer set high hopes were completed, and next day the compressors started to pump air into the compartments adjoining the boiler room to try to gain that much-needed extra buoyancy. New Year's Day passed to the steady rhythm of the air compressors, but the ship gave no sign of responding. The next day, and the next, the air compressors worked ceaselessly to force the water out, with little effect.

The failure of the compressed air to produce the expected results led the salvage officer to try out the four pumps that had been introduced into the boiler room. They might have been pumping in the open sea for all the impression they made. The puzzling thing was that the divers could not find where the water was coming in. Eventually some days later they detected it flowing into the boiler room against one of the bulkheads, but a chaos of twisted metal prevented them from tracing where it came from.

An urgent message from the fleet salvage officer

brought a prompt response from the manager of the Liverpool and Glasgow Salvage Association, who rushed out a first-class diver, Peter Taylor, by air to Cairo to assist on the *Queen Elizabeth*. At this juncture the four divers arrived from South Africa. Never were divers more sadly needed nor gladly welcomed. Working on the diving stage in inky darkness under the guidance of Peter Taylor, they began to burn a way through the ship's bottom, carving away masses of jagged plates with their underwater cutters.

These cutters, so commonplace to divers, are nevertheless a remarkable example of the inventive powers of man. That a flame can be kept alight in the depths of the sea remains something of a miracle. There are two main types of underwater cutters, electric and gas. Both can burn their way through steel plates that are completely immersed in water. The electric cutters form their earth with the plate itself and develop a terrific temperature of about 2,000° C. In the gas cutters used on the *Queen Elizabeth* the flame was forced out at high pressure through a blowpipe, thus driving the water away from the immediate vicinity of the nozzle and enabling the flame to melt through the metal. Needless to add, the correct operation of these cutters demanded much experience and skill on the part of the divers.

Their work was complicated by the presence of fuel oil, which compelled them to use their blowpipes with great care to avoid starting a raging fire with results that might easily have spelled disaster for the divers on the job. They drove ahead for a dozen hours a day until they were ready to drop. When they came to the surface, their attendants stripped off their diving suits and set them out to dry, while the divers went off to enjoy an hour's relaxation before turning in to sleep till dawn. Then came the usual routine of donning their diving suits and slipping down to the stages to resume their fight to save the *Queen Elizabeth*.

By January 28, 1942, they had successfully cut their way through the inner bottom and were able to explore the flooded boiler room which had defied the battery of pumps. The reason was clear. The entire steel floor had been blown away, but by some extraordinary fluke the fittings and machinery had escaped damage.

For three days they made desperate efforts to carry out temporary repairs to enable the boiler room to be cleared of water. Unfortunately the damage was too severe to be surmounted under the prevailing conditions, so the salvage officer was obliged to suspend operations.

Now that she was afloat once more, the *Queen Elizabeth* was moved out to moorings in the harbor on February 1. Within a few days a full-scale test with air compressors and pumps proved that she could pass into the dock as soon as it was ready to receive her.

Throughout the Italians remained unaware of their astounding success. The men in the chariots had been swallowed up in the night and had vanished without trace, while the guns of the *Queen Elizabeth* stuck out menacingly from their turrets as a symbol of the might of the Royal Navy.

Perhaps a musical comedy performed on board the battleship for three days did much to mislead the enemy. Whether it was part of a big bluff may be hotly denied in naval circles, where they argue that you cannot throw thousands of sailors out of work without giving them something to amuse them. Anyway, it was a good show, for which many invitations were sent out to the notabilities of Cairo and Alexandria as well as farther afield to Arab dignitaries and sheiks.

The ship rang with applause as the comedians cracked their jokes and sang their songs. The navy excelled itself. The guests were delighted. They remained in utter ignorance of the fact that the battleship was floating on compressed air. That performance on the *Queen Elizabeth* was a phenomenal success. It was the talk of Alexandria for days. By the time whispers of it reached Italy it had somehow become transformed into a diplomatic reception, which convinced the enemy that there was nothing wrong with the *Queen Elizabeth*. The press conferences which the admiral held on board may also have done much to confirm that the ship was all right.

Thus the astounding luck of the attackers was neutralized by the amazing luck of the defenders. That six men could accomplish so much and so many men could keep it secret are alike unbelievable.

On April 5, 1942, the *Queen Elizabeth* went into

dry dock at Alexandria. At the same time the *Valiant* was passing through the Suez Canal on her way to Simonstown for permanent repairs. Some months later the *Queen Elizabeth* also passed through the Canal on her way to the United States, where she was made battleworthy once more.

There was a strange sequel to the sinking of the *Valiant*. In 1944, after the Allies had defeated Italy, Captain Charles Morgan of the *Valiant* was appointed Rear Admiral commanding the Naval Base at Taranto. One day de la Penne, who had returned from the prisoner of war camp in India, met the English naval officer whose ship he had sunk in Alexandria Harbor. "I couldn't answer your questions when you pressed me in 1941, because I hadn't been able to make fast the charge to your ship's keel. It was only resting on the bottom, and if you had known that, you could have escaped damage by simply going ahead for a short distance," explained de la Penne.

At a later date the Italian chariot expert fought on the side of the Allies and made a brilliant attack on the German ships in the harbor of Spezia. This led Admiral Morgan to recommend his old enemy for a British decoration. As the two countries were still theoretically at war with each other, this decoration could not be granted.

At Taranto in March 1945, however, Prince Umberto of Italy, accompanied by Admiral Morgan, was awarding decorations won in the war by Italian naval officers and men, when he came to Lieutenant

Luigi de la Penne who had won the Medaglia d'Oro al Valor Militare for his successful attack in Alexandria Harbor. "I think this is your turn," said Prince Umberto to Admiral Morgan.

With a smile, Admiral Morgan took the gold medal from its case and pinned it upon the breast of the man who had sunk his ship.

Glory Be! McGlathery

by

Theodore Dreiser

This exciting story by one of America's great novelists is based on actual fact. The leak he describes, which claimed the lives of a dozen men, took place under the Hudson River on July 21, 1880, and a heroic foreman named Peter Woodward was the original of the character called Cavanaugh in the story. The accident, combined with financial difficulties, delayed work for years, but the tunnel was finally completed and became part of the Hudson Manhattan Tubes. Years later, in 1905, a gang foreman named Richard Creegan miraculously escaped death in an adventure that made him a national hero. Dreiser makes use of this episode in the second part of Glory Be! McGlathery. *It is of course a work of fiction, but Dreiser's description of the life of the sandhog, then and now, is completely authentic.*

THE FIRST TIME that McGlathery saw the great river stretching westward from the point where the initial shaft had been sunk he was not impressed by it, or at least not favorably. It looked too gray and sullen, since he was viewing it through a driving, sleety rain. There were many ferryboats and craft of all kinds, large and small, steaming across its choppy bosom, and long, projecting piers, great and mysterious, and over and about all were clouds of gulls and the shriek of whistles and the clang of fog-bells—but McGlathery did not like water.

It took him back to the eleven wretched, seasicky days it had taken him to come from Ireland. But once freed from the mysteries of Ellis Island, he had at last felt dry land under his feet at the Battery and exclaimed: "Glory be, I'm shut av it!"

And he thought he was, for he was mortally afraid of water; but fate, alas! had not so decreed. Water in one form or another had always seemed to pursue him. In Ireland, County Clare, whence he hailed, he had been a ditcher, something remotely connected with water; and here in America, safely settled in Brooklyn, he had no sooner sought work than the best he could get was a job at draining a marsh, and a very boggy and pooly one at that.

Again, he was helping to dig a conduit, a great open sewer, when it was flooded by a cloudburst, a mighty afternoon rainstorm that drove all the workers forth like rats before a volume of water that threatened to drown them all.

Later still he and thirty others were cleaning out a two-compartment reservoir, old and stone-rotten, and just when half of it was empty the old dividing wall broke, and once more he barely escaped with his life by scrambling up a steep bank. It was then that the thought took root in his mind that water, any kind of water, was unfavorable to him. And yet here he was now, facing this great river on a gray November morning, and with the avowed intention of working on the tunnel which was about to be dug under it. Think of it!

It was all due to one Thomas Cavanaugh, a fellow churchman and his foreman these last three years, who had taken a fancy to him and told him that if he came to work on the tunnel and showed himself industrious and courageous it might lead to higher things—viz., bricklaying or plastering, in the guise of cement-molding, down in this very tunnel, or timbering, or better yet, steel-plate joining, which was a branch of the ironworkers' guild and was rewarded by no less a compensation than twelve dollars a day. Think of it!—twelve dollars a day!

Cavanaugh would be his foreman and would look after him. Of course it required time and patience. One had to begin at the bottom—the same being seventy-five feet under the Hudson River, where some very careful preliminary digging had to be done now.

McGlathery had surveyed his benefactor and superior with uncertain and yet ambitious eyes.

"Is it as ye tell me now?" he commented at one place.

"Av course. Whaddaya think I'm taalkin' to ye about?"

"Ye say, do ye? Well, belike it's a fine job. I dunno. Five dollars a day, ye say, to begin with?"

"Yis; five a day."

"Well, a man in my line couldn't get any more than that, eh? It wouldn't hurt me fer once, fer a little while, anyway, hey?"

"It would be the makin' av ye."

"Well, I'll be wid ye. Yis, I'll be wid ye. It's not five I can git everywhere. When is it ye'll be wantin' me?"

The foreman, a Gargantuan figure in yellow jeans and high rubber boots smeared with mud, eyed him amiably, the while McGlathery eyed his superior with a kind of reverence as he felt for no man, unless perchance it might be his parish priest (for he was a good Catholic) or the political backer of his district, through whom he had secured his job. These great men were the leading figures in his life.

And so here he was on this November morning soon after the tunnel had been begun, and here was the river, and somewhere down below in this new shaft was Thomas Cavanaugh, to whom he had to report before he could go to work.

"Sure, it's no colleen's job," he observed to a fellow worker whom he found at the mouth of the shaft, starting down the ladder which stretched below toward an intermediate platform, below which again were another ladder and platform, and below that a yellow light. "Ye say Mr. Cavanaugh is below there?"

"He is," replied the stranger without looking up. "Ye'll find him inside the second lock. Are ye workin' here?"

"Yis."

"Come along, then."

He followed, with his pick and shovel over his shoulder, and carrying his rubber boots and a worn suit of overalls made into a bundle. He reached the bottom of the pit, the sides of which were boarded with huge oak planks sustained by crossbeams, and there, along with several others who were waiting until the air pressure should be adjusted, he entered the lock. The small and yet massive chamber with its heavy iron door at either end, responding so slowly to pressure, impressed him. Here were only the flickering light made by a gasoline torch, and a whistling sound coming from somewhere.

"Ever work under air pressure before, Paddy?" inquired a great, hulking ironworker, looking him over with a genial leer.

"Air what?" asked McGlathery, without the slightest glimmering of what was meant. But not to be outdone by mere words he answered: "No, I never did."

"Well, ye're under it now, two thousand pounds to the square foot. Don't ye feel it?"

He had been feeling an odd sensation about his eardrums and throat, and now admitted it.

" 'Tis air, is it? 'Tis a quare feelin' I have." All at once the hissing ceased.

"Yuh wanta look out fer that, new man," volunteered another, a slithery American. "Don't let 'em rush that stuff on yuh too fast. Yuh're likely to get the bends."

Denis, being ignorant as to the meaning of "bends," made no reply.

"D'yuh know what the bends is?" persisted the other.

"Naw," replied Denis awkwardly, feeling himself the center of a fire of curious observations and solicitation.

"Well, yuh will if yuh ever git 'em—haw! haw!" this from a waggish bricklayer. The group in the lock was large. "It comes from them lettin' the pressure be put on or took off too fast. It twists yer muscles all up, an' does sumpin' to yer nerves. Yuh'll know it if yuh ever get it."

" 'Member Eddie Slawder?" called another gaily. "He died of it over here in Bellevue after they started the Fourteenth Street end. Gee, yuh oughta heerd him holler! I went to see him."

Good news, indeed! Here was a danger not mentioned by Cavanaugh. In his dull way McGlathery was moved by it. Well, he was here now, and they were forcing open the door at the other side of the lock, and the air pressure had not killed him yet. He went with the others through a neatly walled section of tunnel littered with beams and plates and bags of cement and piles of brick, and entered another lock like the first; and there, amid an intricate network of beams and braces and a flare of a half dozen great gasoline lamps which whistled noisily, and an overhanging mass of blackness that was nothing less than the earth under the great river above, was Cavanaugh, clad in a short red sweater and great rubber boots, with his old yellow felt hat pulled jauntily over one ear.

He was talking to two other foremen and a man in good clothes—one of the mighties, no doubt an engineer. Ah, how remote to Denis were the gentlemen in smooth-fitting suits! He viewed them as he might creatures from another realm.

In this lock was a group of nightworkers left over from the night before, ditchers, joiners, earth carriers, and steel-plate riveters, all engaged in the rough and yet delicate task of forcing and safeguarding a passage under the river and now leaving for their day's sleep. The place was stuffy from the heat of the lamps, and dirty from the smear of the black muck that was over everything. Cavanaugh spied Denis as he made his way forward over the widely separated beams.

"So here ye are! These men are just afther comin' out," and he waved a hand toward the forward end of the tunnel. "Get in there, Denis, an' dig out that corner beyond the post there. Jerry here'll help ye. Git the mud up on this platform so we kin git these j'ists in here."

McGlathery obeyed. Under the earthly roof, whose

surface he could but dimly see at the extreme end of the tunnel beyond that wooden framework, he took his position. With a sturdy arm and a sturdy back and a sturdy foot and leg he pushed his spade into the thick mud and threw it up on the crude platform, where others shoveled it into a small car which was then trundled back over the rough boards to the lock and out. It was slow and dirty but not difficult work—so long as one did not think of the heavy river overhead with its great ships and choppy waves.

But Denis was much disturbed by the weight of this heavy volume of earth and water overhead; it really terrified him. Perhaps, after all, he had been overpersuaded by the lure of gold. Suppose it should break through, suppose the earth over his head should suddenly drop and bury him—that dim black earth overhead, as heavy and as thick as this he was cutting now with his spade?

"Come, come, Denis; don't be standin' there lookin' at the roof. It's not goin' to hurt ye. Ye're not down here to be lookin' afther the roof. I'll be doin' that. Just ye tend to yer shovelin'." It was the voice of Cavanaugh, near at hand.

Know, O reader, that the business of tunneling is one of the most hazardous and dramatic of all those included in the field of labor. Underwater tunneling consists, in these latter days, at least, of sinking huge shafts at either side of a river or channel, perhaps one hundred feet within the shoreline, to a depth of, say, thirty feet below the water level, and from these two points tunneling outward under the bottom of the river until the two ends meet near the middle. The exact contact and precise joining of these outer ends is considered one of the true tests of skillful engineering. McGlathery understood this but dimly, and it did not cheer him any.

The safety of the workers depended on the introduction at either end, just at the base of the shafts and then at about every hundred feet or so as the tunnel progressed outward, of huge cyclical chambers, or locks (air locks), of iron, fifteen feet in diameter and closed at each end by massive doors swinging inward toward the shoreline, so that the powerful pressure of air constantly forced outward by huge engines from the shore could not force them open.

It was only by the same delicate system which causes water locks to open and close that they could be opened at all. That is, workmen coming down into the shaft and wishing to pass into the head of the tunnel beyond the lock would first have to enter one of these locks, which would then be gradually filled with air compressed up to the same pressure as that maintained in the main portion of the tunnel farther in. Once this pressure had been reached, they could easily open the inward swinging doors and pass into the tunnel proper. The pressure in the lock, according to who had last used it, would be either that of the section of the tunnel toward the shore or the section of tunnel toward the center of the river.

At first bell cords, later telephones, and then electric signals controlled this lowering or raising of the air pressure in the locks so that either of the doors could be opened. If the pressure in the lock was different from that in your section and you could not open the door (as you could not), you pulled the cord or pushed the button so many times, according to your position, and the air was adjusted to the section of the tunnel in which you stood, and the door could be opened. Once in this next section, the air was raised or lowered, according to your signal, and you could go on to the next.

To Denis, after he had worked here a few days, the digging of his tunnel seemed safe enough. It moved at the rate of eight, sometimes ten, feet a day; but there were days and days when, owing to the need of shoring and timbering and plate setting, or the encountering of rock in front which had to be drilled away, the men with picks and shovels had to be given a rest or set to helping the joiners in erecting those crossbeams and supports which made the walls safe. It was so that Denis learned much about joining, and even drilling.

But in spite of the increased pay this matter of working under the river was a constant source of fear to him. The earth in which he worked was so uncertain; one day it would be hard black mud, another day it would be soft, another silt or sand, according as the tunnel sloped farther under the bed. And sometimes great masses of it fell, not enough to make a hole in the bed of the river, but enough to break the back or bury in the mud any one upon whom it chanced to fall; but usually it was broken by the beams overhead.

One day, some seven months after he had begun this work and his skill had increased to such an extent that he was considered one of the most competent workers in his limited field, the unexpected happened. He was working about the base of two new supports that had just been put in place when he noticed that the earth seemed wetter than usual, sticky and watery and hard to manage. One of the gasoline lamps was hanging close by, and by its light he thought that the ceiling looked silvery gray and beady. He spoke of it to Cavanaugh, who stood close by.

"Yis," he agreed, staring upward, " 'tis wet. Mebbe the air pumps is not workin' right. I'll just make sure," and he sent for the engineer.

But it was the shaft superintendent himself who appeared.

"Everything's all right up there," he said. "Two thousand pounds to the square foot. I'll put on a little more, if ye say so."

"Ye'd better," said Cavanaugh. "The roof's not actin' right. An' if ye see Mr. Henderson send 'im down."

McGlathery and the others, nervous at first but now reassured, worked on. But the earth under their feet became sloppy and some of the silvery frosting on the roof began to drop and even to trickle, and then a mass of sloppy mud fell.

"Back, men!" It was the voice of Cavanaugh; but already the men, always keenly alive to the danger of the situation, had scampered away. Just then an ominous creak from one of the beams overhead gave warning that a catastrophe was imminent, and a pell-mell rush for the lock some sixty feet away ensued. Tools were dropped, and the men fell and stumbled over the beams and between, pushing one another out of the way as they ran, McGlathery a fair second to none.

"Open the door! Open the door!" But that could not be done so quickly.

"Great God, it's comin' down!" cried someone in a panicky voice as three lights in the distance were extinguished.

McGlathery was sweating a cold sweat. Five dollars a day, indeed! He should have known enough to stay away from water. It was always bad luck to him.

"What's the trouble here?" called the engineer as he pushed open the door.

"Git out of the way!"

"For God's sake let us in!"

"Shut the door!" cried those who had reached the other lock and would be safe if only the door was closed.

"No! Wait! Cavanaugh's outside!" yelled another —not McGlathery, you may be sure; he was cowering in a corner.

"To —— with Cavanaugh! Shut the door!" This

from a lumpish ironworker savage with fear.

At this point McGlathery awoke to a sense of duty. True, it was rather weak, but had not Cavanaugh given him this and other jobs? Still, Cavanaugh had persuaded him to come down here, and he shouldn't have done it. But even in his great fear he had manhood enough to feel that it was not right to shut Cavanaugh out. But what could he do? He was but one. Even as he was prodding himself into some action some of the men sprang forward to shut the door, when they faced a gleaming revolver held in the steady hand of Cavanaugh himself.

"I'll shoot down the first man that tries to shut the door before me an' Kelly are in," he bawled, the while he was pulling up this same Kelly from the mud and slime. He fairly threw him into the lock, leaped in himself, and quietly helped to close the door.

McGlathery stood aghast at this show of courage. To stop to help another man in the face of such danger! Cavanaugh was even a better man than he had thought. But why had he persuaded him to come down here when he knew he was afraid of water? And now see what had happened. As they cowered in this safe lock they could hear the crushing of timber and the grinding of brick outside, which told them that where a few moments before had been beams and steel and a prospective passageway for men were now darkness and the might of the river, as it had been since the beginning.

McGlathery awoke to the conviction, first, that he

was a great coward, and, second, that tunnel digging was no job for him.

" 'Tis the last," he commented as he climbed safely out with the others after a distressing wait of ten minutes in the lock. "Begob, I thought we was all lost. 'Twas a close shave, an' I'll go no more below. I've had enough." He was thinking of a small bank account which he had saved, and of a colleen in Brooklyn who was about to marry him. "No more!"

But there was no immediate danger of work being offered. The cave-in had cost the contractors thousands and taught them that mere air pressure and bracing as heretofore followed were not sufficient for tunneling. A new system would have to be devised. Work on both halves of the tunnel was suspended for about a year and a half, during which time McGlathery had married and had had a son born to him. His six hundred dollars had long since diminished to almost nothing; the difference between two and five dollars a day is considerable.

He had not gone near his old foreman in all this time, being somehow ashamed of himself, and so had not fared so well. Hitherto Cavanaugh had kept him fairly well employed, but now there were weeks when he had no work at all, others when he had to work for one-fifty a day. He had a sneaking feeling that if he had shown a little more courage at the time of the cave-in or had even gone to see his old foreman afterward, he might be working now for good pay. Alas, he had not done so, and he felt ashamed to go now. In spite of his marital happiness, poverty began to press him. And then two more children, twins, came.

During this time Henderson, the engineer, had devised a new system of tunneling, which came to be known as the "pilot tunnel." This was an iron tube five feet in diameter which was carried forward on a line with the axis of the tunnel into the ground ahead. When it was driven in far enough to be completely concealed by the earth about, the earth within it was removed. A man could then enter this tube and dig the earth away from in front of it with a pick; another could follow and haul it out with a barrow. It was used exactly as a hub is used in a wagon wheel: beams like spokes were radiated from its sides as a center, and the surrounding earth sustained by heavy iron plates. It was on this plan that the old company had decided to start the work again.

Denis, sitting in his doorway one evening thumbing his way through a newspaper which he could barely read, was able to make this out. Mr. Henderson was to be in charge as before, and Thomas Cavanaugh would return as one of the foremen. Work would begin at once. McGlathery stared thoughtfully at the sky. If Cavanaugh would only take him back!

To be sure, he had come near to losing his life but he was still alive and so were all the others. Why should *he* be so fearful, if Cavanaugh could take such chances? Where else could he make five dollars a day? But that haunting feeling that the sea and all of its arms were against him and would sooner or later do him a great injury, kill him perhaps! He had a recurring sensation of being drawn up or down into water and of being submerged in ooze and choking slowly.

But five dollars a day as against one-fifty or two, or none at all, and an assured future as a tunnel worker, a "sandhog," as such men as himself were called, was a disturbing and alluring thought. After all, he had no trade. He was not a union man. The money he had saved was gone, and he had a wife and three children. His wife agreed with him that tunneling was too dangerous—but after all, the difference that five instead of two a day would mean to them was in the minds of both. After a long period of hesitation he decided that he had better return. After all, nothing had happened to him that other time. He meditated.

A prominent element in McGlathery's nature was superstition. While he believed in the inimical nature of water to him, he also believed in the power of the saints to help or hinder. In the Church of St. Columba of South Brooklyn, where he and his wife were faithful attendants, was a plaster saint of this same name, a co-worker with St. Patrick in Ireland, I believe, who in McGlathery's native town in Kilrush, County Clare, on the water's edge of Shannon, had for centuries now been highly esteemed as having some merit in protecting people at sea or in adventures connected with water. This was due, perhaps, to the fact that Kilrush was directly on the water and required a saint of that kind.

At any rate, before setting out for America McGlathery had made a novena before this saint, craving of him a safe-conduct in crossing the sea, as well as prosperity once he arrived in America. Well, he had crossed in safety and prospered well enough, he thought. At least he had not been killed in the tunnel.

And so one day, after much thought, Denis was to be seen on bended knees before this saint, two blessed candles burning before him in the rack, a half-dollar deposited in the box labeled "St. Columba's Orphans," asking the saint whether, if he returned to this underground work, seeing that necessity was driving him, he would be so kind as to protect him. He felt sure that Cavanaugh would not begrudge him a place. He had always been a good worker.

After seven "Our Fathers" and seven "Hail Marys," said on his knees, and a litany of the Blessed Virgin for good measure, he crossed himself and arose, greatly refreshed. There was a strange conviction in his mind now that he would never come to real harm by the power of water. He bustled out of the church and over to the waterfront where the deserted shaft was still standing, and, sure enough, there was Cavanaugh.

"Yis—an' what are ye here fer?" he asked rather amusedly.

"I was readin' that ye was about to start work on the tunnel again."

"An' so we are. What av it?"

"I was thinkin' mebbe ye'd have a place fer me. I'm married now an' have three children."

"An' ye're thinkin' that's a reason fer givin' ye something, eh? I thought ye said ye was shut av the sea?"

"So I did, but I've changed me mind. I'm needin' the work."

"All right, then. Come tomorrow mornin' at seven sharp. An' mind ye, no worryin' or lookin' around. We've a safe way now."

McGlathery smiled gratefully at his old superior and departed, to return the next morning, still a little dubious but willing. St. Columba had certainly indicated that all would be well with him. But a man is entitled to a few doubts, even when under the protection of the best of saints. He went down with the rest of the men and began cleaning out that nearest section of the tunnel where first water and then earth had oozed and caked, and later helped to install the new pilot tunnel.

Nothing happened, of course, for days and weeks and months. Under Cavanaugh's direction the work progressed swiftly, and in due time he and Denis became good friends again. Denis soon became an expert bracer or timberer, and worth seven a day, which he did not get. Still, he was no longer a mere ditcher. They were soon shifted from day to night work, which somehow was considered more important. Just the same, overhead was the heavy river—he could feel it pushing at him at times, pushing at the thick layer of mud and silt above him.

But nothing happened for months and months. They cleared a thousand feet without a hitch, and McGlathery began to feel rather comfortable. Every night he went down, and every morning he came up, as hale as ever, and every second week a pay envelope was handed him containing the handsome sum of seventy-two dollars. Seventy-two dollars! Naturally, as a token of gratitude to St. Columba, he contributed liberally to his Orphans' Home, a dollar a month, lit a fresh candle before his shrine every Sunday morning after high mass, and bought two lots out on Goose Creek waterfront (on time), on which someday, God willing, he proposed to build a model summer and winter cabin.

And then—! Well, as he thought afterward, it might have been due to the fact that his prosperity had made him a little more lax than he should have been. Anyway, one night, in spite of St. Columba—or could it have been with his aid and consent in order to show his power?—the wretched, sneaky river did him another bad turn, a terrible turn.

It was this way: While they were working one midnight under the new form of bracing and with an air pressure of two thousand pounds to the square foot, which so far had sufficed to support the iron roof-plates which were being put in place behind the pilot tunnel day after day, the concrete men following to put in a form of arch that no river weight could break, the very worst happened. For it was just at the point where the iron roof and the mud of the river bottom came in contact behind the pilot tunnel that the danger spot lay. Cavanaugh was always hovering about that, watching it, urging them to be careful, "takin' no chances with it," as he said.

"Hurry, men!" he would urge. "Up with it now! Up with it! In with the bolts! Quick now with yer riveter —quick! quick!"

And the men, how they worked when there was sufficient space to allow a new steel band to be segmentally set! How they tugged, sweated, grunted, cursed, in this dark, muddy hole, lit only by a few glistering electric arcs! Stripped to the waist, in mud-soaked trousers and boots, their arms and backs and breasts mud-smeared and wet, their eyes bleary—it was an artist's dream of bedlam, a heavenly inferno of toil.

And overhead was the great river, Atlantic liners resting upon it, with thirty, sometimes only fifteen or ten feet of soil between them and its bottom, and this thin strip of mud, sustained by two thousand pounds of air pressure to the square foot, was all they had to protect them, to keep the river from bleeding water down on them and drowning them like rats!

"Up with it! Up with it! Now the bolts! Now the riveter! That's it—in with it, Johnny!"

Cavanaugh's urging voice became like music to them, their gift of energy, their labor song, their power to do, their *Ei Uchnam*.

But there were times when the slow forward movement of the pilot tunnel, encountering difficult earth, left this small danger point unduly exposed to the rotary action of the water overhead, which was constantly operating at the bottom of the river. Sometimes leaks had been discovered, small tricklings and droppings of earth, which brought Cavanaugh and Henderson to the spot and the greatest tension until the evil had been remedied.

The air had a tendency to bore holes upward through the mud, but these had always been stanched with clay or, if serious, with bags of shavings or waste, the air pressure being sufficient to hold these in place if the breach were not too wide. Even when "all hands" were working under a segment wide enough for a ring of plates, one man was always tolled off to "kape an eye on it."

But on this particular evening, after twenty-eight men had entered at six and worked until midnight, seven of them (they were tolled off in lots of seven to do this) were allowed to go up to the mouth of the tunnel to a nearby all-night saloon for a drink and a bite of food. There was always a disturbing transition period every half-hour between twelve and two, when one group was going and another coming, which sometimes resulted in a dangerous indifference which Cavanaugh had come to expect.

On this night one Dowd, ditcher, who was keeping an eye on the breach, was replaced by Patrick Murtha, fresh from the corner saloon, a glass of beer and the free-lunch counter still fresh in his mind. Meditating on the excellence of hot frankfurters and jesting with the men who were about to leave, he forgot to "kape an eye on it."

"Ssssst!"

Came a sound like the blowing off of steam. Cavanaugh was just outside the pilot tunnel showing McGlathery and another where certain braces were to be put so that the pilot tunnel might be pushed forward a few inches and a new ring of plates inserted; but he heard it. At a bound he was back through the pilot hub, his face aflame with fear and rage.

"What the ——'s this?" he was about to exclaim, but seeing a wide breach suddenly open and water pour down in a swift volume, his spirit sank and fear overcame him. "Back, men! Stop the leak!"

It was the cry of a frightened and yet courageous man at bay. Where a moment before had been a hole that might have been stopped with a bag of sawdust (and Murtha was there now attempting to do it) was now a rapidly widening gap through which was pouring a small niagara of foul river water, ooze, and slime. As Cavanaugh reached it and seized a bag to stay it, another mass of muddy earth fell, striking both him and Murtha and half blinding them. McGlathery came staggering back, frightened and not knowing what to do.

"Quick, Denis! Into the lock!" called Cavanaugh, himself holding his ground. "Hurry!" But Denis, realizing the hopelessness of it all and his own danger, thought to run past. He was stopped by the downpour of water and mud. "Quick! Quick! Into the lock! Can't ye see what's happenin'? Through with ye!"

And McGlathery, hesitating by his chief's side, fearful to move lest he be killed, uncertain whether or not to leave his chief, was seized by Cavanaugh and literally thrown through, as were others after him. When the last man was through, Cavanaugh plunged after, wading to his knees in mud and water.

"Quick! Into the lock!" he called, and seeing McGlathery near the door but waiting for him, he added: "In, Denis, in!" There was a mad scramble about the door, floating timbers and bags interfering with them; and then, just when it seemed that all would reach safety, an iron roof-plate overhead, loosened by the breaking of plates beyond, gave way and felled one man in the half-open doorway of the lock, which blocked and pinned it in such a way that it could be neither opened nor closed. Cavanaugh and those who came with him were shut out, and McGlathery, on the other side, could do nothing. A few of them tried to draw the dead man in, all the while calling to Cavanaugh to know what to do. But Cavanaugh was dumfounded and helpless. The plate across the dead man was too heavy, and already the ooze was pouring over him into the lock.

The men in the lock, realizing that they were still in danger of losing their lives, became frantic with fear. There were animal roars of terror. McGlathery, seeing that his Nemesis, water, had overtaken him and was likely to slay him at last, was completely paralyzed. St. Columba had promised him to be sure, but was this not the vision he had had, that awful sense of encroaching ooze and mud? Was he to die thus, after all? Was his patron saint deserting him?

"Holy Mary! Holy St. Columba!" he began to pray. "What shall I do? It's a tight place I'm in now! Tower av ivory! House av gold! Can't we git 'im in, boys? Ark av the covenant! Gates av heaven!"

As he gibbered and chattered, the others screaming about him, some pulling at the dead man and others pulling at the door, the still eye of Cavanaugh outside the lock, waist-deep in mud and water, was surveying it all.

"Listen to me, men!" came his voice in rich guttural tones. "McGlathery! Denis! Are ye all crazy? Take off yer clothes and stop up the doorway! It's yer only chance. Off with yer clothes, quick! Those planks there—stand them up! Never mind us. Save yerselves. Mebbe ye can do something fer us afterward." He saw that if only the gap in the door could be closed and the compressed air allowed to fill the chamber, it would be possible to open the other door into the next section, and so they could all run for safety.

His voice subsided, commanding, never quavering, even in the face of death. About and behind him were a dozen men huddled like sheep, praying and crying. They had got as close to him as possible, still trying to draw upon the sustaining force of his courage, even while they were praying and moaning.

"Yis! Yis!" cried McGlathery, suddenly awakening to a sense of duty and that something better in conduct that he had repeatedly promised himself and his saint. Tearing off his coat and vest and shirt as commanded, he began pushing them into the opening, calling to the others to do the same. In a twinkling bundles were stuffed into the gap and the air prevented from escaping, but the foreman and his men were shut out completely.

"It's awful! I don't like to do it!" McGlathery kept crying to his foreman, but the latter was not so easily shaken. "It's all right, boys," he insisted. And then to the men behind him: "Can't ye stand still an' wait? They may be comin' back in time. Kape still. An' say yer prayers if ye know any, an' don't be afraid."

But although the air pressing outward toward Cavanaugh held the bundles in place, still this was not enough to keep all the air in or all the water out. It poured about the dead man and between the chinks, rising to their waists also. Once more it threatened their lives, and their one hope was to pull open the shoreward door and so reach the chamber beyond; but this was not to be done unless the escaping air was completely blocked or some other method devised.

Cavanaugh, on the other side, was the only one who realized what was to be done. In the panel of the door which confronted him, as in the one they were trying to break open, were thick glass plates, or bull's-eyes, and it was through one of these that he was peering. He saw that the men would not be able to open the farthest door, and his voice was heard over the tumult:

"Break open the outside bull's-eye! Listen to me, Denis! Listen to me! Break open the bull's-eye!"

Why did he call to him? Denis often asked himself afterward. And why did he hear him so clearly? Through the bedlam of cries he heard, but he realized that while the escaping air would improve their chances of opening the door, the lives of Cavanaugh and his helpless companions would certainly be destroyed. The water would rush in from the river, filling up this chamber and the space where Cavanaugh stood. Should he? He hesitated.

"Knock it out!" came the muffled voice of his foreman. "Knock it out, Denis! It's yer only chance." And then, for the first time in all the years he had been working for him, McGlathery heard the voice of his superior waver slightly: "If ye're saved," it said, "try an' do what ye kin for the rest av us."

In that moment McGlathery was reborn spiritually. He ceased to tremble, almost ceased to hurry, and awoke to a new idea: one of undying, unfaltering courage. What! There was Cavanaugh outside, unafraid, and here was he scrambling about like a rabbit for his life! He wanted to go back, to do something, but what could he do? Instead he assumed command here. The spirit of Cavanaugh seemed to come over him and possess him. He looked about, saw a great stave, and seized it.

"Here, men!" he called with a great air of command, "help knock it out!" and with a will born of terror and death a dozen brawny hands were laid on it. With a mighty burst of energy they assaulted the thick plate and burst it through. The air rushed in, the great door gave way before them, and they were swept outward by the accumulated water like straws. Scrambling to their feet, they tumbled into the next lock, closing the door behind them. Once in, they heaved a tremendous sigh of relief, for here they were safe—for the time being, anyhow.

Denis, the new spirit of Cavanaugh in him, turned and looked back through the bull's-eye into the chamber they had just left. Even as they waited for the pressure to lower sufficiently to permit them to open the inner door he saw this last chamber fill with water and mud. It was horrible—his foreman and a dozen fellow workers buried within; but what could he do? Only God, only St. Columba, could tell him—if he were saved—and fifteen other men, the while he had chosen to allow Cavanaugh and twelve others to perish! Had St. Columba done that—or God—or who?

" 'Tis the will av God," he murmured humbly. But why had God done that?

But the river was not done with him yet. Although he prayed constantly for the repose of the souls of Thomas Cavanaugh and his men and avoided the water for all of five years, still there was a sequel. By now McGlathery was the father of eight children and as poor as any average laborer. With the death of

Cavanaugh he had forsworn the sea and all its works and had worked at ordinary house-shoring and timbering, only—well, it was hard to get enough of this work at good pay.

He was faring very badly indeed. And then one day, when he was about as hard up as he could be, from somewhere was wafted a new scheme in connection with the same old tunnel. According to the papers, a celebrated engineer from England had appeared with a new device. Greathead was his name and he had invented what was known as "the Greathead shield," which finally, with a few changes and adaptations, was to rid the tunnel work of all its dangers.

McGlathery, sitting in his doorway overlooking Bergen Bay, read it in the *Evening Clarion,* and wondered if it could really be true. He did not understand this new shield idea even now, but in spite of himself some of the old zest for tunneling came back to him. What times he had had down there! What a life it had been, even if it were a dog's life—and Cavanaugh, what a foreman! And his body was still down there entombed, erect, no doubt, as he had seen him last. He wondered. It would be only fair to dig him out and honor his memory with a decent grave.

Old memories came back to him, old fears, old enthusiasms; and here he was now, with a wife and eight children, earning three a day or less, while tunneling paid seven and eight to such as himself. If this work should start up again and they advertised for men, why shouldn't he go? His life had been miraculously saved on two occasions. Still, would it be again?

In the spring the papers were full of the fact that the work would soon be resumed, and shortly thereafter, to his utter amazement, McGlathery received a card from that same Mr. Henderson under whom Cavanaugh had worked, asking him to come and see him. Feeling sure that it was the river that was calling him, he went over to St. Columba's and prayed before his saint, putting a dollar in his orphans' box and a candle on his shrine. He arose greatly refreshed and heartened, and after consulting with his wife journeyed over to the river, where he found the old supervisor in a shed outside the shaft. He offered McGlathery an assistant foremanship under a new foreman, one Michael Laverty, at seven dollars a day. McGlathery stared in amazement. He an assistant foreman in charge of timbering! And seven dollars sure every day!

McGlathery, listening, was dubious, and yet he was not thinking of the shield now nor of the extra pay, although that played a big enough part in his calculations, but of one Thomas Cavanaugh, mason foreman, and his twelve men buried below there in the ooze; also how he had left him, and how it would be only fair to take his bones out and give him a decent Christian burial.

He owed that much to Cavanaugh, and anyhow hadn't St. Columba protected him so far? And wouldn't he in the future, seeing the position he was in? Wasn't this a call? He felt that it was. But he was nervous and troubled and went home and consulted his wife again, then over to pray in front of St. Columba. Once more spiritualized and strengthened, he returned and told Mr. Henderson that he would come back. Yes, he would come.

Now he felt actually free of fear, as though he had a mission. And the next day he began by assisting Michael Laverty to get out the solid mass of earth which filled the tunnel from the second lock outward. It was slow work and they were well into the middle of summer before the old or completed portion was cleared and the bones of Cavanaugh and his men reached. That was a solemn occasion, the finding of Cavanaugh and his men. They could recognize him by his big boots, his revolver, his watch and a bunch of keys, all near his bones. These same bones and boots were transferred to a cemetery in Brooklyn, McGlathery and a dozen workmen accompanying them.

Thereafter the new shield worked like a charm. It made ten feet a day, and although McGlathery, despite his revived courage, was intensely suspicious of the river, he had little of his old fear. Something kept telling him that henceforth he would be all right. The river could never hurt him any more.

But just the same, about eight months later the river did take one last slap at him, not so fatally as might have appeared on the surface, and whether with or without St. Columba's consent he could not make out. The circumstances were so very odd. This new cutting shield was a cylinder thirteen feet long, twenty feet in diameter, and with a hardened steel cutting edge out in front, an apron, fifteen inches long and three inches thick at the cutting edge. Behind this came what was known as an "outside diaphragm," which had several openings to let in the mud displaced by the shield's advance.

Back of these openings were chambers four feet in length, one chamber for each opening, through which the mud was passed. These chambers had hinged doors, which regulated the quantity of mud admitted, were watertight, and easily closed. Behind these little chambers were many steel jacks, fifteen to thirty, according to the size of the shield, driven by air pressure to drive the shield forward. Back of them came what was known as the tail end of the shield, which reached back into the completed tunnel and was designed to protect the men who were putting in the new plates (at that danger point which had killed Cavanaugh) whenever the shield had been driven forward far enough to permit a new ring of them to be inserted.

The only danger involved in this part of the work lay in the fact that between this lining and the tail end of the shield was always a space of an inch or an inch and a half that was left unprotected. Under ordinary circumstances this small opening would be insignificant, but in some instances, where the mud covering at the top was soft and not very thick, there was danger of the compressed air within, pushing at the rate of several thousand pounds to the square foot, blowing it away and leaving the opening exposed to the action of the water above. This was not anticipated, of course.

Sometime during the following winter, however, the shield encountered a rock which turned its cutting edge. A bulkhead had to be built, once sufficient stone had been cut away, to permit the repairing of the edge. This took exactly fifteen days. In the meantime, at the back of the shield at that little crevice described, two thousand pounds of compressed air to the square foot was pushing away at the mud outside, gradually hollowing out a cuplike depression eighty-five feet long (Mr. Henderson afterward had soundings taken), which extended backward along the top of the completed portion of the tunnel toward the shore. There was then nothing but water overhead, as the engineers now discovered.

The river, being raked by the outpouring of air from below, was rolling gravel and stones about the tunnel top and pounding on it like a drum. It was easy enough to remedy this temporarily by stuffing the crevice with bags; but one of these days, when the shield was repaired, it would have to be moved forward to permit the insertion of a ring of new plates, and then what?

At once McGlathery scented trouble. It was water again, up to its old tricks with him. He was seriously disturbed, and went to pray before St. Columba, and when he was at work he hovered about this opening like a wasp. Mr. Henderson, at Lavery's and McGlathery's request, came down and surveyed it.

"When the time comes to move the shield," he said, "you'll just have to keep plenty of bags stuffed around that opening, everywhere except where the men are putting in the plates. We'll have extra air pressure that day, all we can stand, and I think that'll fix everything all right. Have plenty of men here to keep those bags in position, but don't let 'em know anything's wrong. Let me know when you're ready to start, and I'll come down."

When the shield was eventually repaired and the order was given to drive it just twenty-five inches ahead so that the new plates could be adjusted, Mr. Henderson was there, as were Laverty and McGlathery. Indeed, McGlathery was in charge of the men who were to stuff in the bags to keep out the water. If you have ever seen a medium-sized, red-headed Irishman when he is excited and determined, you have a good picture of McGlathery.

The shield started forward. The extra air pressure was put on; the water began to pour through the crevice; the bags were put in place and stopped most of it, but where the ironworkers were riveting on the plates it poured in so heavily at times that the workers became frightened.

"Come, now! What's the matter wid ye! What are ye standin' there fer? Give me that bag! Up wid it! Do ye think ye're goin' to be runnin' away now?"

It was McGlathery's voice, if you please, commanding—McGlathery, after his two previous experiences! And his very soul was quaking with fear at this moment.

And then—What was it that happened? For weeks after he himself, suffering from the leftover effects of "the bends" in a hospital, was unable to get it straight. Four of the bags of sawdust had burst and blown through, he remembered that—it was a mistake to have sawdust bags at all!—and then, in stuffing others in, they found that they were a bag short, and until something could be found to put in its place, for the water was streaming in like a waterfall, he, McGlathery, defiant to the core and not to be outdone by the river this time, commanded the great thing to be done.

"Here!" he shouted. "The three av ye," pointing to three gaping men near at hand, "up wid me! Put me there! I'm as good as a bag of saadust any day. Up wid me!"

Astonished, admiring, heartened, the three of them jumped forward and lifted him. They held him against the small breach, through which the water was pouring, while others ran off for more bags. Henderson and Laverty and the ironworkers, amazed and amused and made braver themselves by his sheer resourcefulness, stood by to help. And then, if you will believe it, while they were holding him there, one end of the great shield itself was lifted eleven or thirteen or fifteen inches by the tremendous pressure below—

whatever space a medium-size man could be forced through—and out he went, McGlathery and all the bags, up into the river above, the while the water poured down and the men fled for their lives.

It was a terrible moment, as you can well imagine, just long enough to swallow up McGlathery; and then the shield, having responded at first to too much air pressure and now responding to too little (the pressure having been lessened by the escape), shut down like a safety valve and stopped most of the water.

But McGlathery! What of him?

Reader, a miracle!

A tug captain steaming down the Hudson one bright December afternoon was of a sudden astonished to see a small geyser lift its head some thirty feet from his boat, and at the top of it, lying on it, was a black object which at first he took to be a bag or log. He soon made it out well enough, for it plunged and bellowed.

"For the love av Mike! Git me out av this! Oh! oh! oh!"

It was McGlathery, alive and howling lustily, and even trying to swim. For some thirty or forty seconds he had been eddied swiftly along the top of the tunnel at the bottom of the river, and then coming to where the air ricocheted upward he had been hustled upward like a cork and literally blown through the air at the top of the great volume of water, out into space. The sudden shift from so many pounds of air pressure to none at all had brought him down again, and in addition had brought on the severe case of "bends" which carried him to a hospital. But St. Columba had not forgotten him. Although he was suffering horribly and was convinced that he was a dead man, still the good saint must have placed the tug conveniently near, and into this he was now speedily lifted.

"Well, of all things!" exclaimed Captain Hiram Knox, eying him in astonishment. "Where do you come from?"

"Oh! oh! oh!" bawled McGlathery. "Me arms! Me ribs! Oh! oh! oh! The tunnel! The tunnel below, av course! It's dyin' av the bends I am! Git me to a hospital quick!"

The captain, moved and frightened by his groans, made for the nearest dock. It took but a few minutes to get an ambulance, and but a few more to drive McGlathery to the nearest hospital. The house physician, having seen a case of this same disease a few years before, had meditated on it and thought that the hair of the dog must be good for the bite. McGlathery was at once carted off to one of the locks of the tunnel, where he was stared at as one who had risen from the dead. But, better yet, under the high pressure now applied he recovered sufficiently to relieve him of the bends, or the distorted muscles, to become host and tell his story; another trick of the good St. Columba, no doubt.

The whole city, if not the whole country, was astounded by the accident, which all the newspapers published, and McGlathery became a true nine-days' wonder. Indeed the papers were full of this strange adventure, with large pictures of McGlathery ascending heavenward, as well as of the shield.

And again the four weeks spent in hospital were the happiest of his life. For he was interviewed by no less than five representatives of Sunday editors and eleven reporters for city dailies, all eager to know just how it was he had been blown through water and air up through so great a thing as a river, and how he felt en route. It was a triumph. He talked and talked.

Rivers may be smart, but saints are smarter, glory be!

And to top it all off, since his right hand and arm might possibly be crippled for life, and in grateful appreciation of the fact that he had refused to deal with various wolfish lawyers who had descended upon him and urged him to sue for a large sum, he was offered by the company a substantial pension or its equivalent, work at good pay, for the rest of his life, and a cash bonus into the bargain; which solved his very uncertain future for him and put him at ease. Once more the hand or the head of the saint, you see.

But above all there was the peculiar spiritual consolation that comes with the feeling that you have done your duty and a powerful saint is on your side. For if all these things didn't prove that St. Columba had kept faith with him, what could? The river had tried to do its worst and had caused him much fear and pain; and perhaps St. Columba didn't have as much control over the river as he should, or maybe he

(McGlathery) had not always deserved the good saint's support; but nevertheless, in the final extremity he had certainly acted.

If the saint had not been trying to help him, how was it that the tug was just at hand as he arose out of the water two thousand feet from shore? And how was it that the doctor had hurried him off to a lock just in time? Incontrovertible facts, all.

At any rate McGlathery thought so, and on Sundays and holidays, whether or not anything of importance was being celebrated in his church, he might have been seen kneeling before his saint and sometimes eying him with both reverence and admiration. "For, glory be," as he frequently said in narrating the wonderful event, "I wasn't stuck between the shield an' the tunnel, as I mighta been, an' killed entirely. An' it lifted up just enough to let me go out like a cork, an' then, God be praised, it shut down again an' didn't drown the others. But here I am, glory be, an' no worse fer it—though it do be that me hand wrenches me now an' then."

And as for the good St. Columba—

Well, what about the good St. Columba, anyhow?

ORPHAN SHIPS

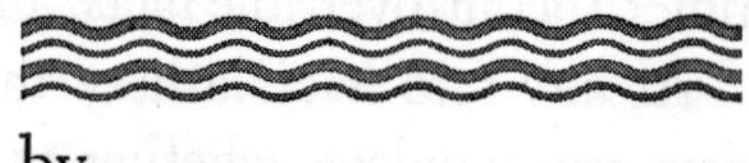

by
Jake Jacobs

In "The Bends," Captain Edward Ellsberg describes the crippling or fatal malady that can attack the underseas explorer. In the following chapter, a famous Pacific Coast diver recounts one of his own adventures in attempting to salvage a steam tug sunk in the waters off Los Angeles. Jacobs later found "snug harbor" as chief diver at Marineland of the Pacific, where he trains dolphins and other marine animals that yearly delight thousands of visitors, but he has never forgotten his brush with death beneath the hull of the Storm King.

SOME SHIPS stay afloat for fifty years or more and some sink within a few years. Taking the total number of all the ships in the world, it has been estimated that the average ship sinks once every twenty-five years. Some go down to unsalvable depths and are paid off as total losses by insurance companies; until broken up by storms or buried under marine sediments, they lie on the bottom, overgrown with seaweed and coral, and provide a home for fish, crabs and octopuses. Sometimes one of these ghost ships rises by herself to haunt the living. There was, for example, the curious case of the *Coos Bay*, which had been buried in sand for thirty-five years and was all but forgotten. Then storms exposed her and she drifted a hundred feet or more, to settle on an oil company's feeding pipelines near Ventura, California.

More vessels sink after collision with near-shore rocks and breakwaters than in the deeper waters of the open sea, and their watery graves are sometimes so shallow that their masts interfere with the passage of other vessels. Some ships sink at their moorings in harbors, some catch fire, some are beached by their crews when in a sinking condition and some are simply abandoned while still afloat. Within a few years our rivers and harbors would become so cluttered with submerged, partly submerged, beached or floating derelicts that, if these wrecks were not removed, shipping would come to a standstill.

Other diving books have told of the search for that rarity, a treasure ship. The very word "salvage" evokes the thought of sunken gold. But actually, divers have found more gold—in the form of drafts on the United States Treasury—in the endless and often dramatic struggle to clear our waterways of these orphan ships.

Under the Rivers and Harbors Act, which became law about sixty years ago, the United States Army Engineers were given the job of keeping the navigable waters of our country free of obstructions. The salvage work itself, however, is done by civilian contractors, who submit competitive bids to a civilian engineer employed by the Army at field offices near each of the major harbors. It is no business to go into on a shoestring, for the low bidder must post a bond equal to the amount the Government agrees to pay on completion of the job, furnish expensive equipment and pay his own divers. Salvage work is beset by many difficulties, and if the job is not completed in the allotted time, the contractor gets nothing for the work he has done and forfeits his bond as well.

Before certifying the job completed, the Engineers must be satisfied that the vessel will not again become a menace to navigation. And so the salvor must either sell her or give her to a responsible person who will repair her and keep her afloat. Or, if nobody wants the vessel, he must get rid of her permanently. Disposing of these white elephants can be a king-sized headache, for some of them weigh as much as 6,500 tons.

If the ship is totally submerged in a harbor, she is usually slung on a cable, lifted to a decks-awash position with pontoons and towed out to a graveyard of dead ships—a deep hole clear of the shipping lanes—where she is filled with rocks and sunk. If a wooden ship is beached where fire can be kept under control, she may be junked out and burned. (The city of Malibu in California asked the Engineers to have the wood from the cargo sailing vessel *Prentice*, which ran aground on its famous beach, stacked beside a highway so residents could pick up free firewood.) If only the superstructure obstructs a shipping lane, it may be blasted.

Occasionally the job takes care of itself, as in the case of the *Mindanao*, which blew up so completely that all the Engineers had to do was certify that the wreckage was sufficiently dispersed. But other explosions have left the fire-blackened hulk intact. One of the most disastrous of these was the explosion of the oil tanker *Markay*, which blew up at a berth in Los Angeles harbor one night in 1946, taking a dozen lives and filling the skies with flame. When the white-hot plates had cooled enough to handle, divers cut them up with torches.

Sometimes an old ship defies all efforts to raise her, like the *Santa Clara*, a sailing vessel that went down in 1939 with one end on the Terminal Island, California, beach. For ten years, one big salvage firm after another worked on her, using methods that had raised many other ships; but she was too rotten to patch up and pump out. Finally, some ingenious youngsters, unhampered by preconceived ideas of how a ship should be raised, hooked onto her with a bulldozer and tore the wreck apart, finishing a job that older and more experienced divers had failed to complete.

Sometimes a salvage job may consist simply of towing a sound but abandoned ship away and delivering her to a new owner. The *Golden State* was a sailing vessel that had been converted into a pirate ship by a movie studio. She appeared in the picture as the *Costa Rica*, and when shooting was completed, the actors deserted her at her berth. All the salvor did was to attach a towline and take her to the other side of the harbor, where, after stripping her of valuable fittings and collecting his salvage fee, he sold her at a good price for conversion into a lumber barge. This may sound like an easy way to acquire a chunk of the taxpayers' money, but there was a catch to it. In order to get this plum, the same contractor had to salvage two other ships, neither of which was quite so easy a job.

One of them was the 795-ton, ex-steam schooner, the *F. S. Loop*, which had been submerged for two years in the main channel of the Los Angeles outer harbor. She was cursed by the crew of every deep-draft vessel that had to pass over her and served as a practice ship for diving-school students. She had the name of a jinx ship, for the five veterans who had bought her on the bottom had brought her a part of the way up several times; but each time she had slipped back and had finally been declared abandoned.

Near her, but clear of the channel, lay the other ship—the 450-ton *Storm King*, a wooden steam tug—with the tip of her bow, her masts and part of her stack projecting at an angle above water. The contractor wanted to float her and hoped to sell her to a firm that would convert her from steam to diesel and recommission her.

By this time I had been diving for weed for about four years. I had also done a little construction diving and now and then had brought up sunken fishing boats—one of them from a depth of 108 feet—using the little *Randall* as both diving boat and tug, and with no more equipment than my diving compressor and a few empty oil drums. On the strength of this experience, I was offered a subcontract to do the diving on the *Loop* and the *Storm King*. That meant I would not get diving wages, but would be paid my share when the ships came up.

To a landsman it might seem that the *Storm King* would be the easier of the two ships to raise. She had only about half the gross tonnage of the *Loop* and, unlike the totally submerged *Loop*, part of her superstructure was well above the low-tide mark. But that is not the way it looks to a diver. Far from hindering, water all around a ship helps by providing lifting capacity that is limited only by the volume of compressed air the tanks can contain. This makes it possible to handle tonnages the most powerful derrick ever built couldn't budge on land.

It took me a comparatively short time to pass cables under the *Loop*, which was resting on an even keel on soft bottom and, with pontoons, to raise her to towing position. But the salvage of the *Storm King* took months of heartbreaking labor, and very nearly cost me my life. In fact, I still have nightmares when I think of the time I was buried alive under the *Storm King*. I have been in much deeper, rougher and lonelier waters, but have never come so close to death as I did 60 yards from shore and less than 35 feet below the calm surface of the busy harbor.

The 120-foot *Storm King* was lying partially on her side and almost standing on end; her stern was down in about 40 feet of water and her bow was up on the beach. When I made an inspection dive, I found that I could go only a little way into her crazily listing passageways. What with the darkness, the debris inside and the angle at which the ship lay, I knew I would never make it to where I had to go—three decks down in the bowels of the ship—without having my feet float. That is one disadvantage of heavy gear, but two skin divers who tried to enter the wreck hadn't got very far either. We decided that it would be much better to do the inside work after we had dragged the ship around on an even keel.

The contractor had already tried with a big crane barge to lift the stern and swing the wreck around parallel to the beach. But the crane exerted only about an 80-ton lift—less than half of what was needed—and only succeeded in tearing a big chunk out of the stern guardrail and planking, which caused us that much extra work later.

We planned to pass a cable under the stern and lift it between a surplus LCI on one side and two pontoons on the other and leave the bow resting on the sloping bottom. The three had a combined lifting capacity of 170 tons but as if to spite anyone who tried to raise her, the *Storm King* had settled where there was hardpan 2 inches under the mud bottom. Hardpan is halfway between clay and rock, and is most obstinate stuff to jet a hole through.

To add to the difficulties, diving in harbors usually means diving blind. A diver may see a little daylight when he first goes down, but after he has walked around and stirred up the mud, he can't see his hand before his faceplate. Diving lights are useless in muddy water, for the particles in suspension block the beam. To do any mechanical work under these conditions, a diver must develop his sense of touch until it is almost as acute as a blind man's. And so, if you ever see a man with normal eyesight working on his automobile engine blindfolded, don't assume he has taken leave of his senses: he may be a diver training himself for a job in dirty water.

With a jetting hose churning up tons of silt, it gets even worse. On the *Storm King* job I was diving in a solution that was half mud and half water. I was using a high-pressure pump that delivered 150 pounds a square inch and a regular fire hose with a diver's jetting nozzle attached. The latter shoots two streams of water, one forward and the other backward, in order to equalize the thrust (a diver is so buoyant that, if he used an ordinary fireman's nozzle, the force of the single stream of water would send him flying backward).

After wrestling with that fire hose in total darkness

for five or six days, I had excavated a tunnel about 15 feet under the tilted ship. The tunnel sloped downward under the keel and then up a little. Its ceiling was the hull itself, and for most of its length it was just high enough for me to kneel in; but at the forward end, where I was digging, it narrowed to little more than the diameter of the hose. I had almost dug my way under the hull and was pushing the hose ahead of me into the narrow end of the ditch and gouging right into the hardpan, when suddenly the nozzle shot forward. I was sure I had broken through and that from then on the job would be clear sailing.

Since I wouldn't be able to see where my nozzle had come out on the other side, I would need a big stream of water to indicate its position, and so I called my tender on the diver's telephone to tell him to speed up the pump. After being picked up by a throat microphone and relayed along a telephone wire spliced to my air hose my voice emerged, much amplified, from a loudspeaker on the deck of the *Randall*. (Navy telephone tenders sometimes wear earphones to screen out the noise of machinery aboard the salvage vessel, but a Navy diver has four or five tenders and dressers. For a civilian who can afford only one man aboard to do all the work, a speaker is a practicable solution—most of the time.)

As soon as my tender complied, I left the hose in the hole, took on some air and floated up to where I could get hold of a guardrail and pull myself up over the sunken ship. On the other side, I felt along the whole length of the hull for my nozzle, but no stream of water was coming through.

I had been thinking that the end of the job was in sight, but now there was no telling how much longer we would have to work before the *Storm King* came up and we could collect on the two-ship contract. I had been working for some time with no income and had run out of money; I was faced with bills for boat repairs, gasoline, mooring and a dozen other things. The contractor wasn't a rich man, either, and he was much deeper in debt than I, since he had staked everything on the completion of his contract. Now the whole job depended on one man diving from a little old boat that was hardly big enough to be a proper lifeboat for the ship we were trying to raise. I seemed very small myself as I felt my way along the towering hulk of the *Storm King*. Somehow I had to figure out how to get that cable under her.

I was still pondering the problem as I floated back over the wreck and crawled into my tunnel to start jetting again, and I was so preoccupied that I forgot the pump was still running at top speed. I had no sooner dragged the hose out of the ditch and freed it from the narrow channel than it began to lash back and forth like a great snake and to wash dirt down on me from the sides of the tunnel.

It happened so fast that all I could do was shout at my tender to stop the pump. But although I shouted again and again, he couldn't hear me over the noise of the pump going at full speed and the air compressor.

Meanwhile, I was being buried alive as the tunnel filled up with mud. I could feel myself being packed in solidly and was becoming panicky. Although I had often warned the young diving-school graduates who worked as my tenders that panic is a diver's worst enemy and that you can get out of almost anything if you and your crew keep calm, my heart was beating wildly and I was so frightened that my mind wasn't working clearly. The clinging muck and the pitch darkness made these the most awful moments I have ever spent on the bottom.

Since I was already on my knees, I was in a good position to do some praying, but all I could think of was Benjamin Franklin's axiom that God helps those who help themselves. I figured that I had carelessly got myself into this predicament and would have to get myself out. Even if my tender shut down the pump so that he could hear me, it might take hours to find another diver and get him down to rescue me. By then my compressor would have run out of gasoline, if it hadn't stopped for other reasons. But theoretically I could jet myself out with the hose if I acted before I was entirely immobilized—and if I knew in which direction to jet. In groping for a way out, however, I had become completely disoriented, and since it was equally black in all directions, there wasn't the slightest visual indication of the exit from the tunnel.

Finally, I gave up trying to get help from topside and put the problem of escape squarely up to myself.

Reaching over my head, I felt the wreck and, when I ran my fingers along the seams, realized that I would have to jet at right angles to those cracks and down under the keel. So I pulled the hose toward me, grasped the nozzle in both hands and somehow managed to reverse it and aim it downhill—how, I will never know, for the pump was still running at full speed and my arms were packed so tightly in mud that they would barely move. Calmness and the strength to control the hose came from reserves I had not known I possessed, and, of course, as long as I kept in my channel, I was able to cut through the mud in it much faster than through the original hardpan. After jetting for what seemed a long time (it was actually only half an hour), I was rewarded by a faint glimmer of sunlight and knew that I had been jetting in the right direction.

When I came up, I didn't tell anyone on the salvage job what had happened. I didn't want to upset my tender or make him feel responsible—when the man topside gets nervous, he's no use to the man on the bottom. If my tender had known I was buried in mud, he might have become excited and tried to drag me out; because of the suction exerted by the muck, he would almost certainly have pulled the hose off my helmet. Nor did I mention the incident to the contractor. I was ashamed of it because a diver should be watching for such things, and it was no credit to my diving ability to have gotten myself buried in mud. If this job had come along a few years later when I had grown more cautious, I would have devised a nozzle extension so I wouldn't have had to go under that hull at all.

The next day I spent no more time than I had to in the tunnel that had nearly become my grave. Having slept on the problem, I nailed one end of a line with a float on its other end to the hull, just above the opening of the tunnel; then, after running my boat around to the other side of the wreck, I dropped a lead line down directly opposite the float. With this as a guide, I was able to jet under the keel and into the old tunnel on the following day.

We pulled several cables through, fanning them out on either side to reduce the strain on the hull, stretched them from the LCI on the starboard side to the pontoons to port. (In shoal water like this, we couldn't simply sink pontoons and then blow them up as we would have done in deeper water. Here we had to use the tides to furnish us with the necessary lift.) At low tide we tightened the cables with a winch aboard the salvage tug until the pontoons on the shoreward side were scraping the bottom; then we waited four hours until high tide lifted the pontoons. The stern was lifted with them, and we dragged it around with other cables stretched to pilings near shore. We repeated this operation night and day, gaining a few feet at a time, until the *Storm King* lay parallel to the shore and was on an even keel, with its full length resting at a uniform depth on the sloping bottom. Her masts and stack were vertical now; the top of her pilot house and after quarters were both awash; and the bow, which had formerly projected from the water, was submerged. Although most of the ship was still underwater, even the sidewalk superintendents along the waterfront, who had predicted that we would never raise the wreck and would have to blast her where she lay, could see that we had accomplished something.

But the real work was only beginning—all this had been only preliminary to blowing her fuel tanks full of air, which is the gentlest method of raising any vessel that uses liquid fuel. It looked as if this method would easily float the *Storm King,* which could steam halfway around the world without refueling and, with her tanks full of oil, was unsinkable. But her tanks now held many tons of salt water, and my job was to go inside the hull and follow the big pipes to the boilers. When I reached the valves used to turn on the burners, I would have to take them apart so the water could drain out when we forced air into the fuel intakes on deck.

Since we had no blueprints of the *Storm King,* we collected as much information as we could from people who were familiar with the layout of ships of her type. The more I knew in advance of where I had to go inside that dark hull, the better, for I would have to plan my route so as not to make a wrong turn and then, to avoid fouling my lines, retrace my steps exactly on the way back.

Nor were blueprints the only thing we lacked. We were chronically short of men and equipment. My tender, a diving-school graduate, was signed on as relief diver; but he and I had also to pitch in on the topside work, which is usually considered beneath the dignity of a salvage diver. And among the things that needed replacing was my old air compressor, which had now done service for well over the thousand dives that are said to make a diver. I had promised myself a new compressor when the ship came up.

At about this time, too, I developed an infection on my knee, probably as a result of dirty water leaking into my dress. The doctor gave me a shot of penicillin and warned me to quit diving until it healed; if I didn't, he said I might lose the leg. But I didn't want to send a young, inexperienced relief diver inside the hull, especially with an unreliable compressor. It seemed better to take chances with my leg than with his life.

So I dressed in and—with wrenches, pliers and a saw at my belt—entered the afterhatch that led to the tow engine compartment. There was some light coming in through its square opening, but my lead-soled shoes slipped and slid on the mossy, waterlogged treads of the wooden ladder. The passageways of the ship were a regular hooraw's nest—mattresses, tables, life jackets and everything but the galley stove floated around my head in a tangled mass that I had to push aside as I walked forward.

Soon the hatch that let in daylight was well behind me, but the water was filled with bioluminescent flagellates called Noctiluca, which outlined everything that moved with a ghostly glow. I only had to wave my hand to set off the most beautiful fireworks against the blackness. It was better than a diving light.

The first impassable obstacle I encountered was a ladder athwart the base of the aftermast. It left just enough room for one man at a time to pass—but not a man in full diving gear. I had to saw out a section of the ladder to get my helmet and breastplate through. The pieces floated upward, edged with luminescence. Then, exhausting air, I floated down through the engine room to the bilges some 20 feet below and started my job. I had just finished with the last valve, when I heard a calm voice on the telephone say, "I guess you might as well come up, Jake. Your compressor just quit."

That was something of a shock. My compressor had failed a good many times before in the open sea, where there was only water between me and the surface. But now, 80 feet or so of my hose and life line were snaked through the passageways of a ship, past all kinds of obstructions.

Luckily, the contractor—a fellow who never expected anything serious to go wrong—was tending lines, my tender having gone to get something to eat.

Some of the conscientious tenders I have had would have started to haul on the lines with everything they had and would probably have sawed off the hose on a sharp corner and killed me in their eagerness to save me. But the contractor calmly waited for me to tell him what to do.

At this comparatively shallow depth, I was still getting plenty of air from the volume tank in the *Randall's* hold and would not have known the compressor had stopped if he hadn't told me about it. One of the volume tanks had rusted out, but the other, I figured, would give me about eight minutes of air—enough time to get out if nothing went wrong. I turned down my exhaust to conserve air and told the contractor that I was coming up and to keep the lines taut, taking them up when they came easily; whatever he did, I told him not to pull hard. He followed those instructions exactly, and moving more slowly than I would have otherwise, since I didn't have time to make mistakes, I made my way out by the same way I had come in, coiling my hose and life line over my arm as I went and paying off the coils as the contractor kept an even, steady tension on them. When I gripped the diving ladder, I was so low on air that I couldn't give myself a final bounce to bring my feet to the level of the bottom rung; I had to be pulled on board by main force, something I never permit to happen normally.

Since I had finished working on the valves of the

Storm King's fuel lines before I had had to come to the surface, we were ready to raise the ship by forcing air into her tanks through the fuel intakes. I was broke and sick, and twice on this job I had nearly been killed, but I was hopeful that it would soon be over. My hopes faded and my spirits hit a new low when I saw the compressed air we forced into the intakes come bubbling up between the deck seams. Evidently a repair job had been going on at the time the ship was abandoned, and the fuel lines must have been disconnected. Now we would have to go through the tedious procedure of patching underwater all possible leaks in the hull. That meant many weeks of hard work with no pay, but it was the only way left to raise her.

The next day I started to nail on plywood patches and batten down canvas over them. The *Storm King* had two rows of portholes; I must have patched forty or fifty of them. Then there was the damage at the stern to be made watertight; the drain pipes opening through the sides from the ship's plumbing to be plugged; and the caved-in fiddley, or skylight, amidships to be covered. What I had learned about buoyancy control in the open sea came in handy, for I had no diving stage to stand on while nailing patches on the sides and had to remain suspended between the bottom and surface. Using a hammer underwater is quite different from using one on land; I had to hold the hammer awkwardly at arm's length so as not to strike my faceplate and take short strokes because of water resistance and so as not to push myself away from my work.

My helper spelled me with this outside work, but since there was no manifold on the compressor, only one of us could dive at a time, and by the time we had finished patching, my knee had healed. Finally we built two cofferdams over a forward and an afterhatch, and the contractor rented six six-inch pumps. We distributed the pumps wherever we could on the parts of the wreck that were above water, lashed them down and dropped the hoses into the cofferdams and the horn-shaped ventilators that led to all the compartments. Then, with our fingers crossed, we started up all the pumps.

It soon became obvious that we were gaining too slowly; evidently there were still big leaks. So I dressed in once more and went down inside from the bow while pumping was going on. Well forward on the first deck down, I found four geysers spouting like Old Faithful from the toilets and filling up the ship almost as fast as the pumps emptied her. Somehow I had missed the drain into which they emptied while I was patching.

I grabbed some pillows that happened to be floating by and stuffed them and cotton from a mattress into the traps. Once I had wedged these plugs in with a wrecking bar and some pieces of two-by-four, the pumps were able to suck up water much faster than it came in, and before I got out of the ship, my head and shoulders were in the air, and I was carrying the full weight of my diving gear.

There were still tons of water in the hold, of course, but now that the deck was above the surface, thousands of small leaks were eliminated, and we gained steadily. We kept those pumps going all night and ran back and forth with cans of gasoline and fresh water for the radiators. We pushed the hoses farther down into the hold as the water level dropped. At three o'clock in the morning of August 12, we stood on the deck of the salvage tug and watched the *Storm King* come up. She was still listing a little but she was unmistakably afloat and rode the rising tide, a proud and sturdy ship. By daylight, there was no danger of her sinking again, and the pumps were stopped. Now you could see how dingy and overgrown she was from her months on the bottom. A broad, dark mark that slanted over her side and across the stack showed where the waterline had been. The *Randall*, which had been made fast to the bow during my last dive, had drifted around over the deck and now was perched high and dry on the big ship.

After we had launched the *Randall*, we tore the patches off the fiddley to let sunlight in. It was strange to go below decks and walk dryshod through passageways that I knew well, yet had never actually seen before. They were strewn with debris that had been floating around my head. Because of my passion for tools, I gravitated to a compartment that had been used by the ship's carpenters—where there was a workbench and over it a row of nails on which hand tools were hanging neatly, covered with rust, except for one of the saws which was as bright as new. This seemed peculiar, until, looking closely, I recognized it as my own. While diving here, I sawed the ladder and hung my saw among the ship's tools. Then I forgot to pick it up on the way out—I'd been lucky to get out myself. It was eerie to come upon my own saw hanging there in this once-dead ship we had brought back to life.

THE WARSHIP *VASA* RETURNS FROM THE SEA

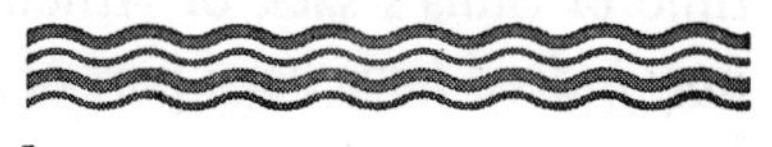

by
Robert Silverberg

There is a type of underwater salvage that, fascinating in itself, has also added greatly to our knowledge of times past. On the ocean bottom lie thousands of wrecks—ships that have succumbed to storms or enemy action, to mutiny or faulty navigation. Most of them have long since disintegrated, a prey to the ceaseless activity of water and microscopic animals. Many are at inaccessible depths, but a few have yielded their secrets to throw new light on bygone civilizations. Of underwater archaeology, the great classical scholar Solomon Reinach once wrote, "The richest museum of antiquity in the world . . . lies at the bottom of the Eastern Mediterranean"; and the first discoveries of this sort took place in that great inland sea. In 1900 two ships carrying Greek sponge divers were forced to take refuge from a storm in a cove off an island near Crete. The mariners occupied their time by diving for sponges and to their amazement found statues of goddesses, men, and horses, made of marble and bronze. Later, in 1907, another group of Greek sponge divers made an even greater find near Mahdia off the Tunisian coast. What they discovered was a Roman ship filled with art masterpieces which had been pillaged at the time of Sulla's sack of Athens in 86 B.C. The cargo may indeed have been part of Sulla's own share of the loot.

Undersea archaeology continues to develop with new techniques and equipment. As in many other phases of undersea exploration, Captain Cousteau has been a leader. Edwin A. Link, inventor of the Link Trainer for airplane pilots, working from a craft specially outfitted for the purpose, has dived at Port Royal, the legendary pirate stronghold in the Caribbean. (Port Royal was called "the wickedest city in the world" and was buried under the sea by an earthquake hundreds of years ago.) One of the most important feats of underwater archaeology was the raising of the warship Vasa, which sank in Stockholm harbor in 1628. That story is told in the following chapter.

AUGUST 10, 1628, was a bright, hot Sunday in Sweden—a good day for a gala event like the launching of a great galleon. And the new warship about to join Sweden's navy was truly magnificent, a sight to inspire fear in the hearts of the foe and pride and awe in the breast of every Swede. The *Vasa* was her name, called after the family of Sweden's warrior-king, Gustavus Adolphus.

The *Vasa* was the new flagship of Sweden's Home Squadron. The Thirty Years' War raged in Europe then, that complex, bewildering struggle that left half the continent devastated when it finally sputtered to its finish in 1648. In 1628 Sweden was not yet deeply involved in the war, but the hero-king Gustav was already planning the brilliant campaigns that would make him the savior of Protestant Europe until his death in battle a few years later. He needed warships to protect the Baltic. The *Vasa* was a giant, 1,400 tons, 165 feet long at the deckline, 40 feet in the beam. "Building small ships is only a waste of young trees," the king had declared.

The *Vasa* bore sixty-four guns—forty-eight massive bronze cannons jutting through double rows of gun ports along her sides, and sixteen smaller guns in the open on the top deck. The hatch of each gun port was decorated with the head of a roaring lion, painted a brilliant gold, its mouth fiery red. The gun decks, too, were painted red, to hide the sight of the blood that would flow on them when the ship engaged in battle. The bowsprit thrust 30 feet outward, and below it, on the prow, a gilded lion, poised to spring, gleamed impressively in the figurehead position.

The brilliant sunlight of that August day in 1628

must have set off the *Vasa*'s gaudy golden and red trim to splendid advantage. Crowds had gathered on the quay to watch the mighty ship get its first taste of the sea. For months, the ship had been moored at the dockside, taking on provisions for a year's voyage. She carried two thousand barrels of foodstuffs and beer, gunpowder, supplies of all sorts. Now it was time for the maiden voyage. The *Vasa* had a crew of 133 sailors. As passengers, three hundred soldiers and their wives and children were aboard.

The *Vasa*'s captain, Severin Hansson, was worried about the design of his ship. It was long and thin—too long, he thought, too thin to support the enormous weight of the 180-foot-high mast and the rest of the vessel's ponderous superstructure. A few weeks before the launching, Captain Hansson had conducted a little test of his own while the *Vasa* rested in her mooring. He had sent a couple of dozen sailors aboard and ordered them to run across the deck from port to starboard. As they did so, their weight made the ship heel more than a foot. As they ran back, she swung two feet back toward portside. Crossing the deck a third time, the sailors caused the *Vasa* to list three feet. Captain Hansson called off the test at that point, fearful that the sailors would capsize the ship altogether.

Sweden's Grand Admiral, Klas Fleming, had watched that test. But he had made no comment. King Gustav was eager to see his proud new ship asail.

It had been three years in the building, and the king had waited impatiently for its completion. No one dared tell him now that a launching might be risky.

So the ceremony proceeded on schedule. At 3 P.M. on August 10, the troubled Captain Hansson gave the order to cast off. A gentle southwesterly breeze fluttered across the harbor at Stockholm. The *Vasa*, carrying many dignitaries who expected to be put ashore the next day at a nearby island, was towed to a point along the south shore of the harbor. Only some of her complement of sails were broken out.

The moment the breeze caught the sails, the *Vasa* veered and heeled wildly to port. The ship's ordnance officer, Erik Jonsson, who was as worried about the ship as his captain, sped belowdecks to make sure the heavy cannon were securely lashed down. If they broke free and rolled to one side of the ship, the *Vasa* would capsize.

The ship righted itself quickly enough, as the passengers moved around to restore the balance. More sail was let out, and as the breeze caught the canvas the stately vessel moved serenely out of the harbor. Captain Hansson ordered the small cannon on the main deck to be fired. A battery on shore boomed a congratulatory reply, and the dockside watchers cheered.

A moment later, a strong gust of wind bellied out the sails, and again the ship listed far to port. A second time, Erik Jonsson hurried below.

"She's going to capsize!" a sailor bellowed.

"Quick!" Jonsson ordered. "Unlash the cannons! Move them to windward!"

The sweating sailors untethered the big guns and strained to push them up the slanting deck and counterweight the heeling ship. But it was too late. Water began to pour through the open gun ports. The cannons broke loose from the sailors' grasp and rolled back, crushing them against the hull. Still the ship heeled to port, until half her bottom had rolled into view. As the water continued to flood the hull, the *Vasa* abruptly went down. The whole episode had lasted but a moment. The cheers of the watchers on shore turned abruptly to gasps of horror and astonishment.

The *Vasa* had gone no more than 4,500 feet on her maiden voyage. Now she rested on the bottom in 110 feet of water. She had nearly righted herself as she sank, and her giant masts jutted above the waves, bearing Sweden's imperial flag on high in cruel mockery.

Boats quickly put out from shore to rescue the sailors and passengers. Most of those aboard were saved, but at least fifty went down with the ship.

The victims were hardly in their graves when the first attempt at salvage was made. The Council of the Realm named Ian Bulmer, an English engineer, to raise the ship. He tried, looping hawsers around the wreck's masts and using horses in a vain attempt to drag the ship from the water. He succeeded in pulling the ship into a completely upright position, but had no luck in getting it from the water. Other would-be salvagers, Swedish, French, English, Dutch, and German, had an equal lack of success. Most of them ended up losing their anchors, cables, and grappling irons, which wound themselves around the wreck.

Meanwhile, a court of inquiry was trying to place the blame for the fiasco. Captain Hansson had been jailed after the sinking. But at the inquiry he mentioned the tests he had run the month before, with sailors moving back and forth over the wobbling deck. "Had they run more times," one of the ship's officers corroborated, "the ship would have capsized at the dock." And Erik Jonsson, who had been badly battered by the water and the sliding cannons, but who had survived all the same, testified that "if she had not been under sail she would even so have capsized . . . as she was heavier topsides than below."

The court of inquiry then turned up two uncomfortable facts: that Grand Admiral Fleming had witnessed the stability tests in July, and that King Gustav himself had approved the plans for the ship. It became awkward to press the inquiry any further. No one in the court had any wish to embarrass people in high places. Captain Hansson and his officers went free, and the matter was quietly dropped. Today, some experts still blame faulty design for the sinking, while the others believe that the tragedy could have been avoided if the cannons had been placed more intelligently.

Be that as it may, the ship had gone down. In 1663, a Swedish group made a new attempt at salvage. They developed a diving bell in which a diver could stand, breathing air at the top of the chamber while using the grappling hooks. Working in fifteen-minute stints in bitterly cold water, the divers, at depths of nearly 100 feet, ripped away the timbers of the main deck and attached grapnels to the cannons. In April, 1664, the first cannons came to the surface, and before they finished, the salvagers had recovered fifty-three of the *Vasa's* sixty-four guns, a valuable prize indeed.

After that, the world forgot about the *Vasa*. It seems hard to believe that so spectacular a catastrophe could slip from everyone's memory. Yet it did. Two and a half centuries passed, and the recollection of the warship's sinking vanished from the minds of men. The great hulk lay in Stockholm's harbor, unknown and unmarked. Now and then a ship would foul her anchors on the wreck, and over the years more than thirty anchors were lost in that way. But no one seemed to know or to care what obstacle on the harbor bottom was causing all the trouble.

The story was rediscovered in the twentieth century. A Swedish historian, Nils Ahnlund, was examining old archives in search of information on an entirely different matter. He had investigated the *Vasa's* sinking, and then found an account of the sensational diving-bell salvage of 1663–64. It was a startling discovery: that a fully outfitted seventeenth century ship lay buried somewhere in Stockholm harbor!

Among those whose imaginations were captured by Professor Ahnlund's revelation was a boy named Anders Franzén. His father, a Stockholm physician, told him the story. Young Franzén would spend his summer vacations, at the family cottage near Stockholm, searching the shallow water for bits of wreckage, and often he would find fragments of old sailing ships, waterlogged but recognizable.

In 1939, Franzén and his family spent the summer cruising off Sweden's west coast, and there he found wood that had been eaten by teredos, or shipworms. Teredos are not really worms at all, but a kind of clam. They burrow their way into submerged wood and actually eat the wood. In the United States alone, teredos do more than $50,000,000 of damage to boats and docks each year. Naturally, they are the bane of the underwater archaeologist, destroying much priceless material.

Young Franzén wondered why the wood he had found near Stockholm showed no sign of teredo damage, while in the waters to the west teredos seemed to flourish and eat everything they could reach. Checking, he learned that teredos could only live in water with a salt content of 0.9 or more. The Baltic's salinity is only 0.7 on the average, and in some places much less.

It was an encouraging discovery. If the waters around Stockholm were free of teredos—why, then, perhaps the *Vasa*, still intact, could be found and lifted!

He kept the idea in the back of his mind for many years. It would be an expensive job, and he certainly did not have the funds for it in 1939. Besides, no one even knew the exact location of the *Vasa*.

Franzén became a petroleum engineer. He studied naval history as his hobby, though, and when SCUBA became available he learned how to skin dive. Compiling a list of more than fifty ships known to have been wrecked off the east coast of Sweden, he narrowed the number to about a dozen, and began looking for them. His first project was the salvage of the *Riksäpplet*, a big warship that had sunk in Dalarö Harbor, near Stockholm, in 1676. With the cooperation of Stockholm's National Maritime Museum, Franzén explored the *Riksäpplet*, which lay in only 50 feet of water. But ice and waves had smashed the ship to fragments, and local people had carried off many of her timbers.

Next he turned to the *Vasa*, which lay in deeper, calmer waters. Professor Nils Ahnlund told him, "Find *Vasa*, and you will have the greatest treasure of all."

But where did the ship lie?

Franzén wrote, "By 1954 . . . I had amassed a huge amount of research data and was ready for an all-out attack. Using borrowed and hired motorboats, I began a systematic sweep of the bottom with grapnels and wire drags. Crews aboard harbor craft became accustomed to the sight of a lonely figure engaged in a strange kind of fishing. They laughed when I brought up old bedsteads, tires, stoves, Christmas trees and the like."

A contour map of the bottom of the harbor had been drawn, using echo-sounding gear, for the benefit of engineers planning a bridge across the harbor. Franzén noted that a large hump was located a hundred yards south of a navy drydock on the harbor island of Beckholmen. Franzén asked the engineers about the hump.

"Oh, it must be just debris left when they blasted out the drydock," they told him.

Franzén turned now to the historical archives. It had occurred to him that King Gustav had been out of the country, fighting in Poland, when the *Vasa* sank. Surely someone must have sent a letter to the monarch telling him about the disaster. Sure enough, he uncovered a copy of the report of the Council of the Realm, dated August 12, 1628, two days after the sinking, bearing the unwelcome tidings to the king. The report said, "And when she came out into the bay by Tegelviken there came more wind into her sails . . . came to Beckholmen sudden, where she entirely fell on her side and sank in 18 fathoms of water."

Beckholmen!

And that suspicious hump near the drydock—was it really only debris of blasting?

Franzén had designed an instrument to help him in his quest—a "core sampler." This was a six-pound steel cylinder, bomb-shaped, and containing a sharp hollow punch in its nose. When he dropped it into the water, the punch would cut a slice out of anything it landed on.

Usually the sampler had brought up nothing but mud. Sometimes it came up with a core of wood, but not ancient wood. The *Vasa*'s hull was made of oak, and oak turns black after a century or more of submersion.

Franzén hurried in a motorboat to the site of the hump on the harbor bottom. It was a fine August day in 1956, almost 328 years to the day since the sinking of the *Vasa*. He threw his sampler overboard. Down it went, more than 100 feet down, and struck. Heart pounding, he reeled it up.

Its punch contained a plug of black, close-grained oak. There could be no doubt now. He had found a ship several centuries old. He had found the *Vasa*.

To make sure he had not simply sampled a single sunken plank, Franzén dropped his sampler over a broad area. Each time it came up with a plug of oak. He went immediately to the Royal Swedish Navy. The Navy's Divers' School was located at the drydock, only 300 feet away. It was an easy matter for him to persuade the Navy to shift its training operations to the site of the *Vasa*.

The first Navy diver to go down was Chief Diver Per Edvin Fälting, a veteran of more than 10,000 hours of diving. Fälting sent up a gloomy report by telephone to the anxious Franzén, waiting on the diving vessel 110 feet above him. "I'm standing in porridge up to my chest. Can't see a thing."

He was about to come up when an accidental twitch on his lifeline from above sent him dropping 20 feet into deeper mud. Reaching out for support, he touched something solid. "It feels like a wall of wood," he telephoned. "It's a big ship, all right! Now I'm climbing the wall . . . here are some square openings . . . must be gun ports."

Climbing higher on the hull, Fälting found the upper row of gun ports as well. This erased the last doubt. No other known wreck in the vicinity had had a double tier of gun ports. This had to be the *Vasa*.

The news electrified Sweden. In a moment the entire country was catapulted three and a half centuries back in time, to the great era when Sweden was a major imperial power in the world and all Europe trembled before the armies of Gustavus Adolphus.

Fälting found that the wreck stood upright, embedded in hard clay to the waterline. The masts, though broken, still thrust surfaceward. In the loose mud covering the upper part of the ship were irons and chains of the seventeenth century salvagers. An underwater television camera, lowered into the mud-clouded water, relayed a blurred but unmistakable image of the mighty ship for those waiting above.

A bold idea took hold in Sweden: why not try to raise the ship in one piece and restore her to her former glory—not as a warship, of course, but as a titanic museum piece?

It would be a formidably expensive job. But no one in Sweden seemed upset by the cost. Sweden's popular king, Gustavus VI, a remote descendant of that old Gustav, was himself a trained archaeologist, and his enthusiasm became infectious.

The Neptune Salvage Company of Stockholm offered to contribute its services free of charge to lift the ship—$500,000 worth of work performed simply to restore this relic of Sweden's past. The Royal Swedish Navy assigned its divers to the operation as a training exercise. Contributions of labor or cash came from all over the country, until the $2,000,000 cost of the project was easily covered.

There were to be two main stages in the salvage operation. First, the wreck should be lifted from her depth of 110 feet and shifted to more accessible waters where she would rest at a convenient 50 feet. There, she would be repaired and strengthened, made watertight so that she could be lifted to the surface.

Captain Axel Hedberg of the Neptune Salvage Company was in charge of the first stage of the project. His plan involved blasting six big tunnels into the bottom next to the *Vasa*'s hull, completely under the ship's keel, and up the other side. Then steel cable could be passed through these tunnels and fastened to salvage pontoons on the surface. When the pontoons were pumped out, they would rise, pulling the cables taut and lifting the ship.

It was, in Anders Franzén's words, "one of the most complicated and perilous" jobs in diving history. The ship's hull was full of rock ballast. If the timbers of the hull gave way, tons of rock would shower down on the divers as they worked. More than two thousand man-hours of work were carried out, though, without a serious injury. The divers—in helmet-suits, not aqualungs, because of the extreme cold of the water—carved the six tunnels with powerful water jets that sliced through the muck at the bottom. Suction hoses sorted through it for material of value. Hundreds of elaborate carved figures, once attached to the hull, had fallen off over the years, and now came to the surface via the suction hoses as the divers worked. Smaller items, such as pewter mugs, clay pipes, a sundial, and coins, came to light during this stage of the work.

Some of the divers were superstitious and believed that the wreck was haunted. *Den Gamle*—The Old One—was the ghost of a sailor who still lived in the wreck. The Old One was supposedly annoyed at being disturbed. To soothe him, the divers would throw copper coins into the water each day before starting work. But still they feared The Old One. One diver, using the water jet to make a tunnel under the keel, suddenly felt his diver helmet, normally almost weightless under water, grow tremendously heavy. He could not understand what was crushing down on him this way.

"The Old One has me," he chattered, panicky, into the helmet telephone.

On the diving barge, Chief Diver Fälting heard him and snapped, "Stop it. Don't panic. If The Old One has you, be calm and go like a man." Then, calming the diver enough to get a description from him of what was happening, Fälting said, "You are caught in a pocket of your own air." The diver was relieved to get such a simple explanation for the occurrence. He crawled out of the tunnel and returned safely to the surface, perhaps still suspecting that it had all been some prank of The Old One.

The Old One stayed his hand, and by August, 1959, after two summers of work, the tunnels were complete and the cables were in place, attached to the salvage pontoons *Oden* and *Frigg*. It was an uneasy moment. Would the old ship, heavily burdened by mud, resist the pull of the cables and come to the surface, or would it collapse into shattered timbers at the first pull?

The signal was given. Pumps began to spew the water from the pontoons. As they emptied, they rose higher from the water, pulling the slack cables taut. A diver went down to inspect the situation.

"*Vasa* has lifted eighteen inches, all in one piece," he reported. "All well."

She was clear of the bottom. With infinite care the salvagers moved the ship toward nearby Kastellholmen (Castle Island). Her keel was four feet above the bottom as she moved up an easy slope. Gradually, she was drawn into shallower water. It took eighteen lifts, over a period of twenty-seven days, before she came to rest in 50-foot water where she could be reached easily for restoration.

The first stage—and the riskiest—was successfully completed. Now came the less dangerous, but infinitely more difficult, task of restoring the *Vasa*. A committee of archaeologists supervised the work. First, divers went down to clear away the debris—the anchors that had been fouled on the wreck, the abandoned salvage equipment of past centuries, and the mud and skeletons of the crew. A dozen well-preserved skeletons were recovered, along with muskets, earthenware, wooden dishes, leather boots, a cockaded felt hat, and even casks of butter. Over a two-year span, the divers boarded up the gun ports, made repairs to the damaged stern of the ship, and caulked all leaks in the hull. Their work made the ship reasonably watertight again.

The archaeologists, meanwhile, were sorting out and classifying the contents of the hull and were taking steps to preserve the perishable wooden statuary by soaking the carvings in arsenic and carbon wax.

The second stage of the salvage operation was finished in the spring of 1961. It was time, now, to lift the *Vasa* to the surface.

Frogmen fastened four inflatable rubber pontoons to the *Vasa's* keel. These would give the ship buoyancy. Steel cables, 9 inches in diameter, were slipped under her hull and attached to jacks on the pontoons. Then the ship was jacked upward out of the water. She rose 5 feet and broke the surface for the first time in 333 years one day in April, 1961. Franzén and Fälting climbed into a small boat and rowed out to inspect the ship as she cleared the water, while on the shore, watchers cheered and a Navy band played a fanfare. Solemnly Franzén clambered out onto the main deck, the first living man to stand on its timbers in three centuries. Then grinning, the unsuperstitious Franzén took a copper coin from his pocket and hurled it into the water-filled hold of the ship. "An offering to The Old One," he explained.

It took a month of cautious coaxing to bring the *Vasa* to shore. Listing slightly to port, she was towed into the drydock at Beckholmen and mounted on a concrete platform. A sprinkler system went into operation to keep the ship wet, for if she were allowed to dry out at this point the timbers would quickly rot.

At the present time, Swedish archaeologists are working to preserve the ship by spraying the wood with polyethylene glycol. This waxy substance will force the moisture from the timbers and keep them from deteriorating. The archaeologists are also still pumping the mud from the ship, shoveling it through wire sieves so that nothing of value will be lost. Later, divers will explore the wreck site in an attempt to recover the elaborate wood carvings which dropped into the mud when the ship sank, as well as the treasure chest of gold that is believed to have been on board. In several years' time, the *Vasa* will be restored completely to her appearance of 1628. The again-proud vessel, gleaming in fresh gold and red paint, will be placed on display in a concrete-and-glass structure near Beckholmen—a museum ship showing exactly what a seventeenth century war vessel was like.

However, the job of restoration may take as many as ten more years.

Among the items salvaged from the hull was a bottle of rum of seventeenth century vintage. In the summer of 1962, when former President Eisenhower visited Sweden and toured the *Vasa*, he was offered a taste of this rum by Anders Franzén. But Ike smilingly declined the offer, and settled for a mere sniff. "It's amazing," he commented.

During his inspection of the ship's carvings and fittings, General Eisenhower noticed that the wooden lion of the ship's figurehead had no tongue. He provoked laughter by remarking, "Maybe it would be better if some of us also did not have a tongue."

The Swedish public seems mostly interested in the ship's treasure and in the skeletons. Archaeologist Anders Franzén finds this an amusing attitude. "Everyone wants to see the treasure, and no one realizes you can see it already. This is the treasure—the ship itself. People are excited by skeletons and gold coins, the two things which historians and scientists care least about. We have graveyards full of seventeenth century skeletons and many collections crammed with seventeenth century coins.

"But now we have a complete seventeenth century community, frozen in place by disaster and preserved by the sea. It will tell us so many things. We don't know how they built ships in the early sixteen hundreds, because there was no science of naval architecture and no one left drawings to tell us. We don't know how the sailors lived aboard ship in those days. We don't know what kind of navigation instruments they used. We don't even know what the Swedish flag looked like in 1628."

As the mud is cleared from the wreck of the *Vasa*, some of these blanks in our knowledge will at last be filled. The giant warship was a miniature city in itself. And now, like Pompeii in Italy or Port Royal in Jamaica, it has been found and uncovered, and soon we will know just how it looked on the day the disaster overtook it.

Part 3

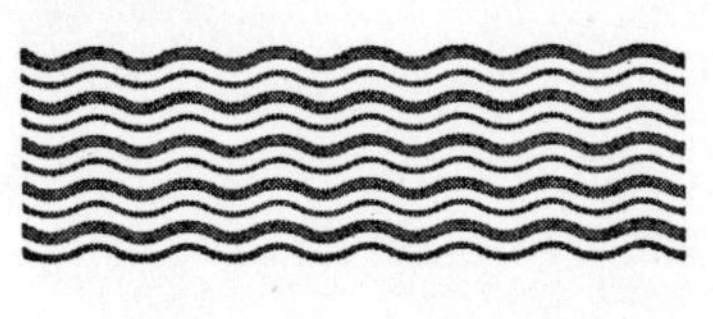

Life Undersea

Jonah and the Whale

from

The Holy Bible

(Jonah I, II)

One of the earliest and most famous undersea adventures is the biblical account of a passenger aboard a ship who is cast into the sea during a storm by a superstitious crew. He is swallowed by a "great fish," and after three days "vomited out upon the dry land." The story has come to be known as "Jonah and the Whale," but the title is not, strictly speaking, accurate. The whale is not a "great fish" but a mammal whose ancestors were probably land animals. It is warm-blooded, it breathes air by means of lungs, its skin is without scales, it reproduces like other mammals and nourishes its young with milk. Was it indeed a whale that swallowed Jonah? The answer remains a mystery.

NOW the word of the Lord came unto Jonah the son of Amittai, saying,

Arise, go to Nineveh, that great city, and cry against it; for their wickedness is come up before me.

But Jonah rose up to flee unto Tarshish from the presence of the Lord, and went down to Joppa; and he found a ship going to Tarshish: so he paid the fare thereof, and went down into it, to go with them unto Tarshish from the presence of the Lord.

But the Lord sent out a great wind into the sea, and there was a mighty tempest in the sea, so that the ship was like to be broken.

Then the mariners were afraid, and cried every man unto his god, and cast forth the wares that were in the ship into the sea, to lighten it of them. But Jonah was gone down into the sides of the ship; and he lay, and was fast asleep.

So the shipmaster came to him, and said unto him, What meanest thou, O sleeper? arise, call upon thy God, if so be that God will think upon us, that we perish not.

And they said everyone to his fellow, Come, and let us cast lots, that we may know for whose cause this evil is put upon us. So they cast lots, and the lot fell upon Jonah.

Then said they unto him, Tell us, we pray thee, for whose cause this evil is upon us; What is thine occupation? and whence comest thou? what is thy country? and of what people art thou?

And he said unto them, I am an Hebrew; and I fear

the Lord, the God of heaven, which hath made the sea and the dry land.

Then were the men exceedingly afraid, and said unto him, Why hast thou done this? For the men knew that he fled from the presence of the Lord, because he had told them.

Then said they unto him, What shall we do with thee, that the sea may be calm unto us? for the sea wrought, and was tempestuous.

And he said unto them, Take me up, and cast me forth into the sea; so shall the sea be calm unto you: for I know that for my sake this great tempest is upon you.

Nevertheless the men rowed hard to bring it to the land; but they could not: for the sea wrought, and was tempestuous against them.

Wherefore they cried unto the Lord, and said, We beseech thee, O Lord, we beseech thee, let us not perish for this man's life, and lay not upon us innocent blood: for thou, O Lord, hast done as it pleased thee.

So they took up Jonah, and cast him forth into the sea: and the sea ceased from her raging.

Then the men feared the Lord exceedingly, and offered a sacrifice unto the Lord, and made vows.

Now the Lord had prepared a great fish to swallow up Jonah. And Jonah was in the belly of the fish three days and three nights.

Then Jonah prayed unto the Lord his God out of the fish's belly,

And said, I cried by reason of mine affliction unto the Lord, and he heard me; out of the belly of hell cried I, and thou heardest my voice.

For thou hadst cast me into the deep, in the midst of the seas; and the floods compassed me about: all thy billows and thy waves passed over me.

Then I said, I am cast out of thy sight; yet I will look again toward thy holy temple.

The waters compassed me about, even to the soul: the depth closed me round about, the weeds were wrapped about my head.

I went down to the bottoms of the mountains; the earth with her bars was about me for ever: yet hast thou brought up my life from corruption, O Lord my God.

When my soul fainted within me I remembered the Lord: and my prayer came in unto thee, into thine holy temple.

They that observe lying vanities forsake their own mercy.

But I will sacrifice unto thee with the voice of thanksgiving; I will pay that that I have vowed. Salvation is of the Lord.

And the Lord spake unto the fish, and it vomited out Jonah upon the dry land.

The Pattern of the Surface

by
Rachel Carson

Only occasionally, as a dolphin plays or a school of fish leaps to escape an enemy below, is the shipboard passenger aware of the teeming life that inhabits many parts of the ocean. Below the surface lies a jungle, in which predatory fish, like tigers, are constantly on the hunt, and in which even such stationary forms as oysters must prey on other living things to survive. How does life, from "microscopic vegetables" to great monsters of the deep, adjust itself to this environment? In vivid detail Rachel Carson paints the picture in this chapter from her great best seller The Sea Around Us.

NOWHERE in all the sea does life exist in such bewildering abundance as in the surface waters. From the deck of a vessel you may look down, hour after hour, on the shimmering discs of jellyfish, their gently pulsating bells dotting the surface as far as you can see. Or one day you may notice early in the morning that you are passing through a sea that has taken on a brick-red color from billions upon billions of microscopic creatures, each of which contains an orange pigment granule. At noon you are still moving through red seas, and when darkness falls the waters shine with an eerie glow from the phosphorescent fires of yet more billions and trillions of these same creatures.

And again you may glimpse not only the abundance but something of the fierce uncompromisingness of sea life when, as you look over the rail and down, down into water of a clear, deep green, suddenly there passes a silver shower of finger-long fishlets. The sun strikes a metallic gleam from their flanks as they streak by, driving deeper into the green depths with the desperate speed of the hunted. Perhaps you never see the hunters, but you sense their presence as you see the gulls hovering, with eager, mewing cries, waiting for the little fish to be driven to the surface.

Or again, perhaps, you may sail for days on end without seeing anything you could recognize as life or the indications of life, day after day of empty water and empty sky, and so you may reasonably conclude that there is no spot on earth so barren of life as the open ocean. But if you had the opportunity to tow a fine-meshed net through the seemingly lifeless water and then to examine the washings of the net, you would find that life is scattered almost everywhere through the surface waters like a fine dust. A cupful of water may contain millions upon millions of tiny plant cells, each of them far too small to be seen by the human eye; or it may swarm with an infinitude of animal creatures, none larger than a dust mote, which live on plant cells still smaller than themselves.

If you could be close to the surface waters of the ocean at night, you would realize that then they are alive with myriads of strange creatures never seen by day. They are alive with the moving lamps of small shrimplike beings that spend the daylight hours in the gloom of deep water, and with the shadowy forms of hungry fish and the dark shapes of squid. These things were seen, as few men have seen them, by the Norwegian ethnologist Thor Heyerdahl in the course of one of the most unusual journeys of modern times. In the summer of 1947 Heyerdahl and five companions drifted 4,300 miles across the Pacific on a raft of balsa logs, to test a theory that the original inhabitants of Polynesia might have come from South America by raft. For 101 days and nights these men lived practically on the surface of the sea, driven by the trade wind, carried on the strong drift of the Equatorial Current, as much a part of the inexorable westward movement of wind and water as the creatures of the sea. Because of his enviable opportunity to observe the life of the surface while living as an actual part of it for so many weeks, I asked Mr. Heyerdahl about some of his impressions, especially of the sea at night, and he has written me as follows:

"Chiefly at night, but occasionally in broad daylight, a shoal of small squids shot out of the water precisely like flying fish, gliding through the air as much as up to six feet above the surface, until they lost the speed accumulated below water, and fell down helplessly. In their gliding flight with flaps out they were so much like small flying fish at a distance, that we had no idea we saw anything unusual until a live squid flew right into one of the crew and fell down on deck. Almost every night we found one or two on the deck or on the roof of the bamboo hut.

"It was my own definite impression that the marine life in general went deeper down in the daytime than during the nights, and that the darker the night was, the more life we had around us. At two different occasions, a snake-mackerel, Gempylus, never before seen by man except as skeletal remains washed ashore on South America and the Galápagos, came jumping clear out of the water and right up on the raft (once right into the hut). To judge from the huge eyes and the fact that the fish has never before been observed, I am inclined to suspect that it is a deep-sea fish that comes to the surface only at night.

"On dark nights we could see much marine life which we were unable to identify. They seemed to be deep-sea fishes approaching the surface at night. Generally we saw it as vaguely phosphorescent bodies, often the size and shape of a dinner plate, but at least one night in the shape of three immense bodies of irregular and changing shape and dimensions which appeared to exceed those of the raft (*Kon-tiki* measured about 45 by 18 feet). Apart from these greater bodies, we observed occasionally great quantities of phosphorescent plankton, often containing illuminating copepods up to the size of a millimeter or more."

With these surface waters, through a series of delicately adjusted, interlocking relationships, the life of all parts of the sea is linked. What happens to a diatom in the upper, sunlit strata of the sea may well determine what happens to a cod lying on a ledge of some rocky canyon a hundred fathoms below, or to a bed of multicolored, gorgeously plumed sea worms carpeting an underlying shoal, or to a prawn creeping over the soft oozes of the sea floor in the blackness of mile-deep water.

The activities of the microscopic vegetables of the sea, of which the diatoms are most important, make the mineral wealth of the water available to the animals. Feeding directly on the diatoms and other groups of minute unicellular algae are the marine protozoa, many crustaceans, the young of crabs, barnacles, sea worms, and fishes. Hordes of the small carnivores, the first link in the chain of flesh eaters, move among these peaceful grazers. There are fierce little dragons half an inch long, the sharp-jawed arrowworms. There are gooseberry-like comb jellies, armed with paralyzing tentacles, and there are the shrimp-like euphausiids that comb the water with their bristly appendages. Drifting where the currents carry them, with no power or will to oppose that of the sea, this strange community of creatures and the marine plants that sustain them are called *plankton*, a word derived from the Greek, meaning "wandering."

From the plankton the food chains lead on, to the schools of plankton-feeding fishes like the herring, menhaden, and mackerel; to the fish-eating fishes like the bluefish and tuna and sharks; to the pelagic squids that prey on fishes; to the great whales who, according to their species but not according to their size, may live on fishes, on shrimps, or on some of the smallest of the plankton creatures.

Unmarked and trackless though it may seem to us, the surface of the ocean is divided into definite zones, and the pattern of the surface water controls the distribution of its life. Fishes and plankton, whales and squids, birds and sea turtles, all are linked by unbreakable ties to certain kinds of water—to warm water or cold water, to clear or turbid water, to water rich in phosphates or in silicates. For the animals higher in the food chains the ties are less direct; they are bound to water where their food is plentiful, and the food animals are there because the water conditions are right.

The change from zone to zone may be abrupt. It may come upon us unseen, as our ship at night crosses an invisible boundary line. So Charles Darwin on H.M.S. *Beagle* one dark night off the coast of South America crossed from tropical water into that of the cool south. Instantly the vessel was surrounded by numerous seals and penguins, which made such a bedlam of strange noises that the officer on watch was deceived into thinking the ship had, by some miscalculation, run close inshore, and that the sounds he heard were the bellowing of cattle.

To the human senses, the most obvious patterning of the surface waters is indicated by color. The deep blue water of the open sea far from land is the color of emptiness and barrenness; the green water of the coastal areas, with all its varying hues, is the color of life. The sea is blue because the sunlight is reflected back to our eyes from the water molecules or from very minute particles suspended in the sea. In the journey of the light rays downward into the water and back to our eyes, all the red rays of the spectrum and most of the yellow have been absorbed, so it is chiefly the cool, blue light that we see. Where the water is rich in plankton, it loses the glassy transparency that permits this deep penetration of the light rays. The yellow and brown and green hues of the coastal waters are derived from the minute algae and other microorganisms so abundant there. Seasonal abundance of certain forms containing reddish or brown pigments may cause the "red water" known from ancient time in many parts of the world, and so common is this condition in some enclosed seas that they owe their names to it—the Red Sea and the Vermillion Sea are examples.

The colors of the sea are only the indirect signs of the presence or absence of conditions needed to support the surface life; other zones, invisible to the eye, are the ones that largely determine where marine creatures may live. For the sea is by no means a uniform solution of water; parts of it are more salty than others, and parts are warmer or colder.

The saltiest ocean water in the world is that of the Red Sea, where the burning sun and the fierce heat of the atmosphere produce such rapid evaporation that the salt content is 40 parts per thousand. The Sargasso Sea, an area of high air temperatures, receiving no inflow of river water or melting ice because of its remoteness from land, is the saltiest part of the Atlantic, which in turn is the saltiest of the oceans. The polar seas, as one would expect, are the least salty, because they are constantly being diluted by rain, snow, and melting ice. Along the Atlantic coast of the United States, the salinity range from about 33 parts per thousand off Cape Cod to about 36 off Florida is a difference easily perceptible to the senses of human bathers.

Ocean temperatures vary from about 28° F in polar seas to 96° in the Persian Gulf, which contains the hottest ocean water in the world. To creatures of the sea, which with few exceptions must match in their own bodies the temperature of the surrounding water, this range is tremendous, and change of temperature is probably the most important single condition that controls the distribution of marine animals.

The beautiful reef corals are a perfect example of the way the inhabitable areas for any particular class of creatures may be established by temperatures. If you took a map of the world and drew a line 30° north of the equator and another 30° south of it, you would have outlined in general the waters where reef corals are found at the present time. It is true that the remains of ancient coral reefs have been discovered in arctic waters, but this means that in some past ages the climate of those northern seas was tropical. The calcareous structure of the coral reef can be fashioned only in water at least as warm as 70° F. We would have to make one northward extension of our map, where the Gulf Stream carries water warm enough for corals to Bermuda, at 32° north latitude. On the other hand, within our tropical belt, we would have to erase large areas on the west coasts of South America and Africa, where upwelling of cold water from lower ocean levels prevents the growth of corals. Most of the east coast of Florida has no coral reefs because of a cool inshore current, running southward between the coast and the Gulf Stream.

As between tropical and polar regions, the differences in the kinds and abundance of life are tremendous. The warm-water temperatures of the tropics speed up the processes of reproduction and growth, so that many generations are produced in the time required to bring one to maturity in cold seas. There is more opportunity for genetic mutations to be produced within a given time; hence the bewildering variety of tropical life. Yet in any species there are far fewer individuals than in the colder zones, and here we have no dense plankton swarms like the copepods of the Arctic. The pelagic forms of the tropics live deeper than those of the colder regions, so, with little surface life to feed on, there are no seals in the tropics, and compared with the clouds of shearwaters, fulmars, auks, whalebirds, albatrosses, and other birds seen over far northern or southern fishing grounds, there are few birds.

In the cold-water communities of the polar seas, fewer of the animals have swimming larvae. Generation after generation settle down near the parents, so that large areas of bottom may be covered with the descendants of a very few animals. In the Barents Sea a research vessel once brought up more than a ton of one of the siliceous sponges at a single haul, and enormous patches of a single species of annelid worm carpet the east coast of Spitsbergen. Copepods and swimming snails fill the surface waters of the cold seas, and lure the herring and the mackerel, the flocks of sea birds, the whales, and the seals.

Sea life in the tropics, then, is intense, vivid, and infinitely varied. In the cold seas it proceeds at a pace slowed by the icy water in which it exists, but the mineral richness of these waters (largely a result of seasonal overturn and consequent mixing) makes possible the enormous abundance of the forms that inhabit them. For a good many years it has been said categorically that the total productivity of the colder temperate and polar seas is far greater than the tropical. Now it is becoming plain that this is not necessarily true. In many tropical and subtropical waters, there are areas where the sheer abundance of life rivals the Grand Banks or the Barents Sea or any antarctic whaling ground. These are the places, as in the Humboldt Current or the Benguela Current, where upwelling of cold, mineral-laden water from deeper layers of the sea provides the fertilizing elements to sustain the great food chains.

And wherever two currents meet, especially if they differ sharply in temperature or salinity, there are zones of great turbulence and unrest, with water sinking or rising up from the depths and with shifting eddies and foam lines at the surface. At such places the richness and abundance of marine life reveals itself most strikingly. This changing life, seen as his ship cut across the pathways of the great currents of the Pacific and the Atlantic, was described with vivid detail by S. C. Brooks:

"Within a few degrees of the equator, the scattered cumulus clouds become thicker and grayer, a confused swell makes up, rain squalls come and go, and birds appear. At first there is only a greater abundance of storm petrels, with here and there petrels of other kinds hunting along utterly indifferent to the ship, or small groups of tropic birds flying along with the ship, off to one side or high overhead. Then scattered groups of various petrels appear, and finally for an hour or two there are birds on every hand. If one is not too far from land, a few hundred miles perhaps, as in the case of the south equatorial drift north of the Marquesas, one may also see multitudes of sooty or crested terns. Occasionally one sees the grayish-blue form of a shark gliding along, or a big purplish-brown hammerhead lazily twisting around as though trying to get a better view of the ship. Flying fish, while not so closely localized as the birds, are breaking the water every few seconds, and bewitch the beholder by their myriad sizes, shapes, and antics, and their bewildering patterns and shades of deep brown, opal blue, yellow and purple. Then the sun comes out again, the sea takes on its deep tropical blue, the birds become more and more scarce, and gradually, as the ship moves on, the ocean resumes its desert aspect.

"If it were daylight all the time, this same sequence might be seen in a more or less striking fashion twice or perhaps even three or four times. Inquiry soon reveals that this sequence marks the time of passing the edge of one of the great currents . . .

"In the North Atlantic ship lanes the same play is staged with different actors. Instead of the equatorial currents there are the Gulf Stream and its continuation, the North Atlantic Drift, and the Arctic Current; instead of confused swell and squalls of rain there are slicks and fogs. Tropic-birds are replaced by jaegers and skuas; and different species of the petrel group, usually here spoken of as shearwaters and fulmars, are flying or swimming about, often in great flocks . . . Here, too, perhaps, one sees less of sharks and more of porpoise racing with the cut-water or doggedly hurrying, school after school, toward some unguessable objective. The flashing black and white of the young orcas, or the distant sudden spurt and lazy drift of a whale's spouting, lend life to the water, as do the antics of flying fish, distant though they be from their traditional home in the tropics . . . One may pass from the blue water of the Stream, with floating gulf weed (Sargassum), and perhaps here and there the iridescent float of a Portuguese man-of-war, into the gray-green water of the Arctic Current with its thousands of jellyfish, and in a few hours back again into the Stream. Each time, at the margin, one is likely to see the surface display of that abundance of life which has made the Grand Banks one of the great fisheries of the world."*

The central oceanic regions, bounded by the currents that sweep around the ocean basins, are in general the deserts of the sea. There are few birds and few surface-feeding fishes, and indeed there is little surface plankton to attract them. The life of these regions is largely confined to deep water. The Sargasso Sea is an exception, not matched in the anticyclonic centers of other ocean basins. It is so different from any other place on earth that it may well be considered a definite geographic region. A line drawn from the mouth of Chesapeake Bay to Gibraltar would skirt its northern border; another from Haiti to Dakar would mark its southern boundary. It lies all about Bermuda and extends more than halfway across the Atlantic, its entire area being roughly as large as the United States. The Sargasso, with all its legendary terrors for sailing ships, is a creation of the great currents of the North Atlantic that encircle it and bring into it the millions of tons of floating sargassum weed from which the place derives its name, and all the weird assemblage of animals that live in the weed.

The Sargasso is a place forgotten by the winds, deserted by the strong flow of waters that girdle it as with a river. Under the seldom-clouded skies, its

* From *The Condor*, vol. 36, no. 5, Sept.–Oct. 1934, pp. 186–7.

waters grow warm and heavy with salt. Separated widely from coastal rivers and from polar ice, there is no inflow of fresh water to dilute its saltiness; the only influx is of saline water from the adjacent currents, especially from the Gulf Stream or North Atlantic Current as it crosses from America to Europe. And with the little, inflowing streams of surface water come the plants and animals that for months or years have drifted in the Gulf Stream.

The sargassum weed is a brown alga that lives attached to rocks along the coasts of the West Indies and Florida. Many of the plants are torn away by storms, especially during the hurricane season. They are picked up by the Gulf Stream and are drifted northward. With the weeds go, as involuntary passengers, many small fishes, crabs, shrimps, and innumerable larvae of assorted species of marine creatures, whose home had been the coastal banks of sargassum weed.

Curious things happen to the animals that have ridden on the sargassum weed into a new home. Once they lived on a rocky shore, a few feet or a few fathoms below the surface, but never far above a rocky bottom. They knew the rhythmic movements of waves and tides. They could leave the shelter of the weeds at will and creep or swim about over the bottom in search of food. Now, in the middle of the ocean, they are in a new world. The bottom lies two or three miles below them. Those who are poor swimmers must cling to the weed, which now represents a life raft, supporting them above the abyss. Over the ages since their ancestors came here, some species have developed special organs of attachment, either for themselves or for their eggs, so that they may not sink into the cold, dark water far below. The flying fish make nests of the weed to contain their eggs, which bear an amazing resemblance to the sargassum floats, or "berries."

Indeed, many of the little marine beasts of the weedy jungle seem to be playing an elaborate game of disguise in which each is camouflaged to hide it from the others. The Sargasso sea slug—a snail without a shell—has a soft, shapeless brown body spotted with dark-edged circles and fringed with flaps and folds of skin, so that as it creeps over the weed in search of prey it can scarcely be distinguished from the vegetation. One of the fiercest carnivors of the place, the sargassum fish Pterophryne, has copied with utmost fidelity the branching fronds of the weed, its golden berries, its rich brown color, and even the white dots of encrusting worm tubes. All these elaborate bits of mimicry are indications of the fierce internecine wars of the Sargasso jungles, which go on without quarter and without mercy for the weak or the unwary.

In the science of the sea there has been a longstanding controversy about the origin of the drifting weeds of the Sargasso Sea. Some have held that the supply is maintained by weeds recently torn away from coastal beds; others say that the rather limited sargassum fields of the West Indies and Florida cannot possibly supply the immense area of the Sargasso. They believe that we find here a self-perpetuating community of plants that have become adapted to life in the open sea, needing no roots or hold-fasts for attachment, and able to propagate vegetatively. Probably there is truth in both ideas. New plants do come in each year in small numbers, and now cover an immense area because of their very long life once they have reached this quiet central region of the Atlantic.

It takes about half a year for the plants torn from West Indian shores to reach the northern border of the Sargasso, perhaps several years for them to be carried into the inner parts of this area. Meanwhile, some have been swept onto the shores of North America by storms, others have been killed by cold during the passage from offshore New England across the Atlantic, where the Gulf Stream comes into contact with waters from the Arctic. For the plants that reach the calm of the Sargasso, there is virtual immortality. A. E. Parr of the American Museum has recently suggested that the individual plants may live, some for decades, others for centuries, according to their species. It might well be that some of the very weeds you would see if you visited the place today were seen by Columbus and his men. Here, in the heart of the Atlantic, the weed drifts endlessly, growing, reproducing vegetatively by a process of fragmentation. Apparently almost the only plants that die are the ones that drift into unfavorable conditions around the edges of the Sargasso or are picked up by outward-moving currents.

Such losses are balanced, or possibly a little more than balanced, by the annual addition of weeds from distant coasts. It must have taken eons of time to accumulate the present enormous quantities of weed, which Parr estimates as about 10 million tons. But this, of course, is distributed over so large an area that most of the Sargasso is open water. The dense fields of weeds waiting to entrap a vessel never existed except in the imaginations of sailors, and the gloomy hulks of vessels doomed to endless drifting in the clinging weed are only the ghosts of things that never were.

SHARK! PATTERN OF ATTACK

by
Thomas Helm

Of all the bad actors of the deep—moray eel, sting ray, octopus, stone fish, barracuda—none strikes such terror as the predator whose presence is heralded by the cry of "Shark!" Its ways are unpredictable, its attack can be remorseless, and it is one of man's most hated enemies. Few observers have made a more careful study of this tiger of the waters—its origins, its history, the various kinds of shark (some extremely vicious, some relatively harmless)—than the author of the chapter that follows. Thomas Helm has hunted sharks both commercially and for sport and has had a lifelong interest in the out-of-doors. He here explains the ways in which sharks attack, the dangers to avoid, and why it is never safe to trifle with a shark.

IT IS a matter of record that the incident of shark attack on people in the waters surrounding the United States has taken a decided upswing. From the end of the first World War until 1958 there were only twenty-five shark attacks reported in United States coastal waters. In round figures that averages about one attack every year and a half. Beginning with the spring of 1958, the number of attacks suddenly skyrocketed from one every eighteen months to thirty in the same period of time.

Even with this phenomenal increase, the thinking person will look at the figures from a statistical standpoint and conclude that shark attack is just about the least of human worries. Forty to fifty thousand people are slaughtered annually on the nation's highways, multitudes die in floods and fires, and thousands of others are killed by machinery. Almost everyone can point to a relative or friend whose death was caused by an auto accident, drowning, a fire, a fall or some other "normal" means of untimely death. After the initial pangs of sorrow are dulled by time, the tragedy is accepted as one of the hazards of human existence. This same acceptance is far from true, however, when the victim has been killed by a creature from the sea. This may possibly be due to the fact that civilization long ago agreed that the human body should not be eaten by man or beast. It is interesting to consider how little space newspapers of the nation devote to a single traffic victim compared to that allotted to someone who has been killed or seriously injured by a shark.

Why there has been the sudden upsurge in shark attacks in our heretofore *safe* waters has all of the scientists baffled. While there are a lot of logical theories, no one has yet come up with an undisputable answer. Of course, in recent years more and more people have begun turning to the sea as an almost new-found source of recreation. But it is doubtful that the spring of 1958 produced an increase in coastal visitors sufficient alone to account for the larger number of shark attacks. Some point to the skindiver and say that he is responsible. At first glance this seems to be a likely answer, for skindiving is, with the possible exception of boating, the fastest growing sport in the world today. Prior to World War II the only people who could go beneath the sea long enough to look around were deep-sea divers, and they were few and far between. A man named Jacques-Yves Cousteau changed all of that when, during the war, he developed the aqualung. It—and other equipment like it—has come to be known generally as a self-contained underwater breathing apparatus or SCUBA. Grandmothers and teen-agers, bank presidents and factory workers are discovering a strange new world beneath the sea that is now open to them through this medium.

Nearly seven million people are today diving deeper and staying longer in regions normally inhabited by sharks, and it would seem logical that these are the people who are responsible for the sudden increase in attacks. Statistics do not agree, however. True, the skindiver comes in for his share of shark attacks, but the average swimmer is still the number one target.

One theory that is at least interesting, if not entirely logical, is that the food supply of the shark has been reduced and because of this he has begun to look on man as a substitute. True, there is little doubt that the heavily fished coastal regions are producing far less fish with each succeeding year, but while this may be a source of lament to commercial and sport fishermen, certainly it is hardly enough of a loss to cause sharks to start eating people. Supporters of this theory, however, are reluctant to give in, and offer as further argument their belief that sharks follow a set pattern that is governed by the seasons and is similar to the migratory flights of waterfowl and the roamings of such animals as the reindeer. Suppose, they say, that a shark has been accustomed for eons on end to arriving off of the lower California beach at a particular season each year to feast on a certain type of fish. When he arrives, he finds that man has depleted the schools with hook and net. Would not the shark, driven by hunger pangs, attack any swimmer he chanced upon?

Another group of theorists attribute the increase in the number of attacks to a rise in the shark population. Students of nature find this idea worth more than casual consideration, for it has long been known that almost all forms of living creatures occasionally experience what is commonly known as population explosions. Even the human race is currently involved in such a condition, and science finds itself at a loss to say just why. Is it possible that simultaneously the sharks are breeding more rapidly and producing more surviving young at a time?

There is still another theory, and this also has to do with a phenomenon that science can not satisfactorily explain. The waters around the United States—the world, for that matter—have suddenly grown warmer. As a matter of fact, the average temperature of water along the Atlantic and Pacific coasts has been increasing at a rate of about one degree for each passing year since 1958! In the over-all picture this might not seem important. But consider man himself. The temperature extremes between which man feels comfortable are indeed shallow. At 69° he begins looking around for his jacket and above 72° he prepares to take it off.

It has been proved under laboratory conditions that certain species of sharks cease to feed when the water temperature drops below 68° and that they either lie dormant or migrate to warmer climes. It has also been proved that even a few degrees increase in temperature will step up their metabolism and increase their hunger correspondingly.

At this point it is obvious that there is no sure answer for the rapid increase in the number of shark attacks on humans in the past few years. Whether it is caused by more sharks, warmer water or an influx of swimmers, the sum total is still the same. For one who loses his leg, arm or life to a shark, statistics count for little. It is far more important to know how to prevent such a tragedy in the first place.

Even the earliest military students were taught that to know one's enemy was to win half of the battle, and the swimmer or skindiver who knows something about sharks is a long way ahead of the game.

It is generally considered that sharks feed in only two ways. One of these is known as the individual feeding pattern and the other is called the mob feeding pattern. After a good part of a lifetime spent in pursuit of Old Man Shark, I am willing to concede that these two are the most common, but investigation has convinced me that there is still a third, which might be called the man-eater pattern.

In his book titled *Man-Eaters of Kumaon,* Major Jim Corbett described a man-eating tiger as one compelled through stress of circumstance beyond its control to adopt an alien diet. This stress, Corbett said, might be caused by wounds, old age or both. Once tasting human flesh and realizing how easy it is to obtain, he continues, the tiger forsakes natural prey and concentrates on humans.

It is entirely possible that certain sharks have learned to depend on a plentiful abundance of human bathers to assuage their appetites when cruising the waters around the United States. The number of attacks that have occurred in the same areas along our coast line adds impetus to this theory.

The term "individual feeding pattern" deals with

the way most sharks collect their intake of food. It is simple and uncomplicated. The lone foraging shark swims in an unhurried manner, either cruising near the bottom or just under the surface. Along the way he picks up a crab, sting ray, squid, small turtle, or any other type of food he can overtake. Occasionally his sensitive olfactory system catches the scent of blood. Instantly his movements quicken, for he knows an injured creature offers him an easy and sometimes large meal. Often the scent of blood comes from a school of fish—such as mullets, herring or sardines—which is being attacked by bluefish, mackerel, tuna, or maybe a herd of porpoise. With unerring accuracy the lone shark is led to the spot where the shoal of food fish is being feasted upon by its hungry hunters. This is an old game to the shark and he scurries about in the wake of the feasting fish, picking up the bits and pieces that drift down from the pelagic banquet table. Most predatory fish are wasteful and seldom bite at their quarry more than once. That part which is inside the mouth goes down the gullet while the head or tail section is left to drift toward the bottom. There is little doubt that a shark would be content to trail around behind a school of tuna or other such expert hunters, except for the fact that he cannot swim fast enough to keep up with them.

Again the lone shark may pick up the faint scent of blood coming from a female porpoise as she gives birth to her young. This moment is perilous in the life of a porpoise, for to become a mother she must sink to the bottom while she endures her labor pains and then be ready to carry her newborn quickly to the surface for its first breath of air before it drowns. If the male porpoise is not on guard, the chances are good that the shark will rush in and gobble up the baby porpoise before its parents realize what is happening.

If conditions are right when a foraging shark happens upon a lone swimmer, he may attack. Because man, however, is not his normal prey, the average large shark will deliberate for a considerable length of time before attacking. It has been this hesitancy which has gained him the reputation of being a coward. By the same token, this hesitancy has been the means of salvation for countless swimmers who have found themselves in unpleasantly close contact with a shark.

A friend of mine, who is an ardent and experienced spearfisherman, recently had a harrowing experience with a 12-foot brown shark in the deep channel off the south end of Anclote Key near Tarpon Springs, Florida. Don and his partner had speared a big grouper and were carrying it back to their boat when they spotted the large shark circling around them. Blood from the dying grouper was staining the water and it was obvious that the shark was becoming more excited with each passing minute. In a sudden rush he bore in for an attack. Instead of dropping the fish and kicking frantically for the surface, Don shoved the grouper toward him. The shark grabbed the fish and in the next few seconds the two spearfishermen scrambled into the safety of their skiff. They wisely decided to come back another day when the competition was not quite so stiff.

No one knows with certainty just what a lone shark will do. It is reasonably safe to assume that under normal conditions he will not make an attack on a human without some provocation. The question is, what constitutes provocation?

Unhappily, a lone shark may attack a swimmer for any of a dozen different reasons. Suppose, for instance, that the water is clouded by silt and a passing shark catches sight of an outflung hand or a kicking foot. To his dim eyesight, the flash of a hand or foot can look exactly like a wounded fish, and the shark may try to grab it before it gets away.

Under another set of circumstances, a swimmer may have cut his foot on a chunk of coral or a broken bottle. While the wound may not be sufficient to drive him from the water, even a small amount of blood advertises his presence. When the shark comes to investigate, his nose leads him up to the wounded foot and he takes a bite. The swimmer struggles, the teeth bite deeper, and all at once there is lots of blood in the water. The shark becomes more excited and he begins to attack his victim in a frenzy.

In some cases a shark is as solitary as a tomcat on the prowl; but sharks also swim in schools, and when the scent of food is in the water, they join forces as would a pack of hungry wolves. They appear to lose all of their normal caution as they vie with one another for the food. Examples of this mob feeding occur frequently when large quantities of garbage are disposed of at sea and when commercial fishing boats rid their decks of the noncommercial fish hauled up in their nets. It is during this mob feeding when wounded swimmers, such as shipwreck survivors, stand the least chance.

Even during this writing, my wife and I were unexpectedly exposed to a typical example of the mob feeding pattern. We had anchored our small boat in a shallow cove on the lee side of Caladesi Island near Clearwater, Florida, and were preparing to wade ashore when we noticed an unusual number of sting rays drifting about the flats. Some were average in size, measuring little more than 15 inches from tip to tip, while others were almost 4 feet wide.

"That one is having young," my wife said, pointing to a big ray resting on the botton only a few feet off our stern.

Sure enough, several small sting rays the size of pie tins were bursting out of her and flapping clumsily away. I was watching in fascination when the water around the boat boiled and I caught sight of a 5-foot shark driving in. In a matter of seconds it had picked up one of the newborn sting rays, and in the minutes that followed other sharks appeared in the area. Often they were in water so shallow that half of their bodies were exposed. Time after time they struck at the newborn sting rays, and occasionally we could see the old mother rays flapping their way to the surface with a hungry shark close behind. By conservative estimate there must have been more than a thousand rays that had chosen this particular cove in which to have their young. Under normal conditions this might have been a safe seagoing maternity ward, but the school of what I took to be mako sharks had got wind of the operation and was transforming the area into a scene of wholesale carnage. Having good reason to dislike the whole sting ray population, I was almost glad to see the sharks feeding on the young rays. Needless to say, we remained in the boat until all signs of sharks were gone.

The third type of attack is the one made by the rogue or confirmed man-eater. Whether certain sharks, like certain tigers, develop a taste for human flesh has not yet been positively determined and probably never will be. There is, however, good reason to suspect that such sharks do exist. On occasions far too numerous to ignore, there has been a series of attacks in given areas, and when notes are compared it is obvious that at least the same type and size shark was responsible.

The history of shark attacks dates back just about as far as written and pictorial records extend. In V. M. Coppleson's book, *Shark Attack*, published in Australia in 1958, there is a picture of a vase discovered in excavations at Lacco Ameno, Ischia, which is believed to have been painted about 725 B.C. Drawings on this vase show a sailor being devoured by a sharklike fish.

After the discovery of the New World, the Spaniards began to call the shark *tiburon*. Antonio Pigafetta, who sailed with Vasco da Gama around Africa, wrote that the tiburon have teeth of a terrible kind and eat people when they find them in the sea either alive or dead. Olaus Magnus of Sweden printed a picture of a shark attack in the middle of the sixteenth century. It showed the victim being rescued by a kindly ray. No one has yet been able to explain why the old Swede thought a ray of any type would come to man's rescue. Perhaps he just wanted his illustrated story to have a happy ending.

In 1580 one seafarer wrote an account of a man being killed by a tiburon. He noted that the seaman was swept overboard but managed to grab a trailing line. Before he could be hauled back to the ship by his mates, however, a shark cut the man to pieces. "That," he concluded, "surely was a grievous death."

From time to time, in first one part of the world and then another, scientists have undertaken the task of compiling lists of authenticated shark attacks. Notable among these has been the aforementioned V. M. Coppleson, whose work was concerned primarily with the shark problem in Australian waters. In 1959 Dr. Robert F. Hutton, marine biologist with the Florida State Board of Conservation, prepared a paper which listed in great detail all incidents of shark attack in Florida waters up to 1959. At the present time the American Institute of Biological Sciences is engaged in a world-wide study on the subject.

Chambers of commerce in certain resort areas will

make every effort to squelch as many reports of shark attack as possible. In those areas, however, it is fortunate that the research scientists do not have to depend on those sources for information. Instead, they gather their facts from a number of other outlets, such as the local hospitals, police departments and newspapers.

Quite logically, however, no state wants to gain the reputation of having a shark-infested coast line. For that matter, what inland state would peacefully submit to being branded with the stigma of being overrun with rabid dogs or disease-carrying ticks or anything else designed to drive away the tourist trade?

It has been sagely considered that all shark attacks can never be recorded, for if a shark is completely successful in his attack, there is no trace left. He has, in effect, left no clues. Almost any popular resort beach along the waters surrounding the United States, Spain, South Africa or Australia has a certain number of unexplained disappearances. If someone is last seen swimming in the surf and then fails to turn up in a respectable amount of time, it is logical to assume that he drowned and that the body will be washed ashore or found floating in the next few days. When this fails to happen, there are those who will suggest that the missing person was devoured by a shark. As a matter of fact, this is in all probability the case, for the human body seldom fails to rise to the surface shortly after a normal drowning, and the odds are ten to one that it will quickly be washed ashore thereafter.

The chief life guard at a popular California beach

recently remarked that no less than four people disappeared completely there in a single summer. It is possible that they were grabbed by hungry sharks.

In the subtropical waters which surround the United States it is generally considered that the months of June, July and August are the most dangerous. While attacks have occurred earlier and later, there are invariably more swimmers in the water during these three months and sharks are known to be more plentiful in this period. Laboratory tests have proved that the dangerous types of sharks give up feeding almost entirely when the water temperature drops to 60° F, but there are few bathers who would consider going swimming in water that cold. Therefore, this information is of little solace to the average swimmer.

There are numerous ways that swimmers, fishermen and skindivers actually invite or encourage a shark to attack, and the most outstanding of these mistakes might well be considered.

Swimming alone is a dangerous practice at any time. While sharks have been known to come into a group of bathers and single out a victim, attacks are more often made on people who are removed from the normal swimming area. Added to this, when there are numbers of people present, the chances of rescue are greater and there is more likely to be someone on hand who is capable of administering first aid.

There are two reasons why the swimmer is safer in clear water than that which has been clouded by roiled sand or silt. First, the shark apparently feels a sense of security in murky water, and since he hunts primarily with his nose, poor visibility does not bother him. Second, the chances of a swimmer's sighting a shark are far greater in clear rather than cloudy water.

A good place to avoid is a stretch of beach where the water shoals off quickly, as on the side of a channel or near passes between two islands. Such deep-water passages are natural feeding grounds for sharks. What is more, a shark knows that his safety lies in deep water, and if he happens to spot a swimmer close to the edge, he may be tempted to take a bite, especially since he knows he has a safe route of retreat close by.

Many people with a sense of false bravado will refuse to leave the water even after a shark of dangerous size has been sighted. These are the same people who will take shelter under a water tank or beneath a lone pine tree in the middle of an electrical storm. With a bit of luck they can perform their grandstand play many times, but the law of averages is constantly working against them.

Fish is the natural food of any shark, and the smell of dead or dying fish in the water is a sure attraction to sharks, if any are in the vicinity. The skindiver who ties his catch to his belt is asking for trouble. He can be severely bitten by even a small shark if it suddenly finds the fish to which its nose has led it. The safest policy is to get the speared fish back to the boat or shore as quickly as possible. The surface angler who decides to clean his catch while still out on the bay and then washes his hands and knife over the side after he has "chummed" the water with fish scraps is also asking for trouble. I once had a frightening experience while doing just this.

I had caught about a dozen fine speckled trout while fishing on a small Florida bay. It was getting along toward sundown and I decided to clean my catch and put the fish in the ice chest before I returned to the dock. I began splitting each fish open, emptying the intestines over the side, and removing the head. After each operation I swished the fish about in the water beside the boat before tossing it into the ice chest. The next to the last one I was cleaning slipped out of my hand while I was washing it in the water. Grabbing a small aluminum paddle, I reached out in an attempt to recover the sinking fish. Almost at the instant I touched it, a four-foot hammerhead shark appeared and struck a vicious blow at the tip of the paddle. Pulling it back aboard, I found that the blade had been scored and dented with teeth marks.

Reflecting on what had happened, I could not help considering myself exceedingly lucky. The fish scraps I had been tossing over the side had apparently drawn the small hammerhead up close to the boat. As long as his source of food was uncontested, he was content to remain out of sight and wait for the scraps to drift down. When I reached out after the fish with the paddle, however, he quite logically thought that another fish had appeared to join the feast and he was going to have none of that. I still shudder when I think what could have happened if I had made a grab for the trout with my hand instead of the paddle.

A moonlight swim may be romantic and refreshing, but it is also a good way to wind up with part or parts of your anatomy in a shark's stomach. A shark is more prone to come in much closer to shore at night than during the day. This, in fact, is a common practice of many sea creatures. What is more, it seems that a shark's feeding activity is stepped up to a marked degree during full-moon periods. Consequently, it is advisable to revel in the moonlight on the safety of the beach and enjoy the surf the following morning.

Unfortunately, there are no cut-and-dried rules for a swimmer, skindiver or fisherman to follow in case he is attacked. For that matter, it is often hard for one to know with positive assurance when a shark is actually attacking until it is too late. While it may be far from the truth, the safest course is to consider any approaching shark as an attacking shark.

A few years ago my wife, Dorothy, and I were fishing on the northwest coast of Florida near Port Saint Joe. We were in a small, 12-foot skiff powered by a 2½-horsepower outboard motor. Admittedly, this was not much of a saltwater fishing craft, but we were in waters close to shore while the surf was light. We had found excellent early morning sport with a school of mackerel, and along about ten o'clock we cruised in toward the beach. When we were in water a little over waist deep, I shut off the engine and we jumped over the side.

"You hold the boat out here in the water," I said, "and I'll go back to the camp and pick up some soft drinks and sandwiches for lunch." This seemed like a simple request, and when I returned some ten minutes later to find Dorothy standing on the beach with the skiff broached to and the propeller and lower housing grinding into the sand, I was understandably disturbed.

"Three sharks came after me," Dorothy explained, obviously shaken. "I was standing there with the boat pointed seaward and all at once a shark brushed against my leg and almost knocked me off my feet. Then two more came in and began bumping against the boat."

With an irritated chuckle, I tossed the sandwiches and drinks into the boat and started to push it back into deep water. Suddenly a seven-foot shark cleaved the water only inches from my side. I struck out at it with my left hand. Instantly the shark spun around and came back toward me. The water was hardly more than waist deep, but he was obviously swimming freely. He bumped me on the right side and I felt the smart of salt water against abraded flesh. A moment later I saw another shark of about the same size pass close beside the boat and then a third shark crash against the hull. Releasing my grip on the boat, I cautiously waded ashore. For the next fifteen minutes we stood on the beach and watched the three sharks cruising around while our small boat rocked about in the shallow surf.

Encounters with sharks while skindiving have impressed me with the fact that obviously dangerous ones can often be held at bay if the diver does not allow himself to be stampeded. It is possible that the human body exudes a musk in time of great fear, and this, coupled with a headlong flight for safety, may give a shark or any other predatory creature an open invitation to attack. It has often been suggested that wild animals and even vicious dogs can quickly sense when a person is frightened and will accordingly press an attack that might otherwise have been averted had the person stood his ground.

Interesting to note is the fact that Pliny the Elder wrote in the first century that the best way to avoid being attacked by a shark (he called it a dogfish) is to swim straight for him, thus frightening him off. In the following two thousand years, scores of other recommendations were advanced, and then in June of 1960 the shark symposium which appeared in *Skin Diver* magazine wound up with the same recommendations.

In the case of shark attack, it is necessary to remain calm. Admittedly, this is a remedy more easily prescribed than carried out. Nevertheless, it should be remembered that the shark is accustomed to finding food among creatures which have been disabled in one way or another.

How does one go about the business of remaining

calm and unruffled if a dangerous shark has appeared and given indication of attack? The answer is not easy to find. What is offered here can be little better than suggestions gleaned from consultations with scores of people who have been molested or attacked by sharks.

When a shark comes near, the bather should start swimming with slow, deliberate strokes toward the beach or his boat. In ninety-nine cases out of a hundred, the shark is merely curious, and as long as the swimmer is moving along with no undue effort, the chances are that it will hesitate to attack. Upon reaching shallow water, the swimmer should never give vent to his pent-up emotions and make a frantic scramble to cover the last few yards separating him from the safety of the beach. The shark is constantly on the lookout for a wounded prey and any violent thrashing may be misconstrued as the dying struggles of a fish. Fatal shark attacks have often been known to occur in water less than three feet deep, so shallow water is not a safety factor.

If several people are swimming when an approaching shark is sighted, it is well to draw close together. Even after reaching water shallow enough for wading, they should remain in a tightly knit group as they make their way to the beach. In this manner they may represent one very large creature to the shark.

It has also been suggested that ducking the face below the surface and making a loud roaring sound will occasionally cause an aggressive shark to draw back. If any fish are being carried, they should be dropped as quickly as possible.

A final and important *don't* concerning sharks is this: *don't* ever grab hold of one, no matter how close it comes. Movie heroes can get away with this in guarded tanks with drugged sharks, but it should be remembered that the free-swimming shark in the ocean is nothing but a wild and often savage beast. His reactions are generally governed by impulse and he would be as quick to strike back as a Bengal tiger if someone were foolish enough to grab the big cat by the tail.

ULYSSES AND OTHERS

by

Captain J. Y. Cousteau

with James Dugan

There are innumerable tales, some accurate and some products of the imagination, dealing with the behavior of fishes, the signs of intelligence they display, the friendships and enmities between men and denizens of the deep. The characters range from Moby Dick, the legendary white whale of Melville's novel, to Pelorus Jack, a dolphin which regularly escorted ships crossing the straits between two main islands of New Zealand and which in 1904 was accorded the signal honor of being protected against capture by an act of the New Zealand Parliament. Many fantastic accounts survive from antiquity and remain impossible to prove. One modern episode is vouched for by the most trustworthy observers. In the following chapter we are introduced to Ulysses the friendly grouper, who became the pet of members of the vessel Calypso, *and whose reported demise brought sorrow to an entire ship's crew.*

LUIS MARDEN and I were gamming on the after-deck as *Calypso* ranged south on a soft night in the Indian Ocean. He was anxious to dive on tropical reefs and photograph as many species of fish as possible. I pointed to a streak in the water and said, "A flying fish. In a day or so, you'll be able to shoot thousands of them without getting wet. We're coming to the big girdle of flying fish wrapped around the Equator. They'll come big as mackerels and land on board as high as the spar deck."

The *National Geographic* correspondent said, "You're kidding. They can't fly more than two feet off the surface. I've seen plenty of them in the Caribbean."

Marden staggered back from a blow on the head. A half-pound flying fish lay flapping on the deck. I led Luis to a mirror and showed him fish scales sticking to a red bruise on his forehead. Hardly had the laughter at his discomfort ended than we heard nightmare cries from Malle's cabin. A flying fish had entered his open port and fallen, struggling, on his sleeping face. In the morning we picked up ten pounds of them for breakfast.

A newly stranded flying fish looks rather ordinary

except for its distinctive asymmetrical tail. Unfold its pectorals and you will see the long, gauzy, metallic blue wings that sometimes glint with iridescent orange patterns. By day, flying fish rarely collide with a vessel, but skitter away from it. Their flight seems always to be motivated by the threat of a predator. In *Calypso's* underwater observatory we had a pursuer's view of flying fish. They swam just beneath the surface, their white bellies blending into the shiny ceiling. When alarmed, they picked up speed and steered sharply up through the surface.

We could follow the rest from the deck. Breaking water, they immediately spread their wings and warped them to increase the lift. The long lower tail lobe remained in the water, sculling rapidly to drive the fish to take-off speed. They flew into the wind close to the water where ground assisted flight. The flying fish does not beat its wings like a bird. It is a glider with an "outboard motor" that it dips into the water several times during a flight. Many times we saw flying fish traveling out of the water for more than 600 feet. The animal used its last spurt of propulsive energy to deceive the pursuer about the point of re-entry. After flying a long straight course, it veered off into crosswinds or even doubled back downwind until it had to go below again.

The gliding fish thrives despite constant attacks by swift enemies like jacks and dorados by day and jet-propelled squids by night. The very act of flight also exposes it to sea fowl, which gather hungrily when the underwater beaters send up flying fish. This is a species that succeeds in life despite continuous aggression underfoot and overhead.

During the winter of 1955 *Calypso* was making a battered, uneasy passage from Diego Suarez, Madagascar, to Aldabra in the southeast trades. I decided to take shelter for three or four hours at Assumption, the southernmost island of the Aldabras, to wash the salt cake off the ship and give the hardworking men some rest before we bucked on to the big atoll, where we could only expect the same state of constant alert we had experienced on our first visit to that ship-hating island. The chart showed that the west coast of Assumption was protected from the trades by a bay in the scimitar-shaped land. And the depths were good for anchoring. As we approached in white water, we saw the high filao trees on the island bending their tops in the wind. *Calypso* descended from rolling crags into calm water where mild zephyrs played around our subsiding decks. Across the bay there was a crescent of alabaster sand. Falco, who was leaning over the forepeak, called back, "The water is crystal clear." I heard mechanical hissing on the afterdeck. Already Jean Delmas was filling the triple-tank blocks. I dropped anchor in 60 feet of water close to shore and got word around that we would have a look at the place and sail for Aldabra in the afternoon.

Delmas treated himself to the first dive. He went head down through the looking glass into the most enormous vistas he had ever scanned in the underwater world. The sea was transparent for 200 feet in any direction. Delmas had been with *Calypso* in the Red Sea reefs, at Antilythera, and at Aldabra, but had not seen anything approaching the scenes that Assumption Reef offered to the human eye. The corals were richer. The fish were thicker and had no fear. They came to Delmas in a multitude, wearing all the colors that can be imagined. He stumbled back on deck under his heavy gear and said to me earnestly, "Let's stay here instead of going to Aldabra. This is the place to make friends with fish. You must tell all the divers never to carry a gun, never to swim fast or use menacing gestures, never to set off a dynamite cap. Let's take food down to them. You'll see something."

Before I could reply, the newly beatified St. Francis of the Fish left me for the galley and began dicing lunch leftovers to take to them. Marden returned with the second relay of divers, and he too preached Assumption. "Jacques," said he, "it is incredible down there. It is the ocean turned inside out. When I tried to take close-ups of the fish, they came too near to stay in focus. When I backed off, they came with me."

The third pair underwater—the veteran, objective men, Dumas and Falco—came out babbling. I couldn't get a sober report from any of them. I hefted an aqualung onto my back.

Underwater, while I still had a hand on the ladder, I was enslaved by Assumption Reef. I climbed back and announced that we were going to stay there as long as our fresh water lasted. Somebody said, "Let's start rationing it now, so we can stay longer." The first divers at Assumption Island were Albert Falco, Frédéric Dumas, Émile Robert, Luis Marden, Henri Plé, Octave Léandri, Jean-Louis Teicher, Louis Malle, Pierre Goupil, Edmond Sechan, Dr. Denis Martin-Laval, Simone, Delmas, and myself.

The structure of the island was classical. A shallow fringing reef, sparkling with sunshine and dancing color, extended 200 to 300 feet from the white beach. It dropped off rather abruptly into a chaos of standing coral and grottoes for about 200 feet, where a gray sedimental plain faded away into the ocean. Every foot of the slope was a model of extravagance, with the richest cocktails of coral that you could expect to find in the reefs of the world. Along the bank, mixing in friendly anarchy, were most of the species of fish we had met in a thousand other places and a quantity of new ones we had never seen before—as well as some kinds that no one had ever seen. Among the animals there prevailed a spirit of mutual interest and confidence. It was almost as though the struggle for life was suspended and the Peaceable Kingdom had been translated into the bosom of the waters.

During the next forty days our thirteen divers spent so much time with the fish that we became lean and haggard, hardly able to drag ourselves up the ladder to eat and sleep, but at the same time impatient for the next descent. Our skins became blotched with unhealed wounds. We developed unbearable itches from coral burns and the stings of invisible siphonophores.

Delmas, whom we called "Tonton," had an attack of fever. He would shake and rattle his teeth for several hours and then dive again. The surgeon could not identify the illness—it had no relation to malaria. We called it "Tontonitis." Before long, one after another, we were stricken with Tontonitis, which seemed to be a marine allergy.

Here and there on the deep floor were cones of sand from six to twelve inches high which occasionally erupted like miniature volcanoes, presumably from the spout of a hidden animal. Again and again, Marden tried to photograph an eruption. As he lay on his stomach with his camera trained on a cone, all about him the other volcanoes spouted, but Marden's always remained dormant. After several days of this I went down to see what was keeping him busy. He was flat on the floor, looking with disgust at a nonperforming volcano. I pointed my forefinger at one nearby and flipped my thumb like a trigger. It erupted. On board, Luis begged for my secret. I said, "I just had the fantastic luck to point at the thing when it was about to squirt." After many more patient hours Marden got his shot. We excavated several of the mounds to find the animal that was producing the jets, but we could not find one. It probably retreated into subterranean galleries deeper than we could dig with our hands.

Émile Robert, a stout Marseilles pastry cook turned professional diver, was Marden's assistant, bodyguard, and timekeeper. Once Robert came up from a session on the lower reef and described a small fish he had seen that had disappeared before Marden had a chance to photograph it. The fish was covered by a perfect grid of tile-red and white squares, for all the world like a checkerboard. Robert's "checkerboard fish" story drew pointed remarks about rapture of the deep. He was infuriated by our disbelief and, when below, dragged others to the haunt of the checkerboard fish. He could not produce it and the kidding got worse.

One day I was setting up a movie sequence around a deep black gorgonian, using the big flood lamps. All the divers were working on the shot. There came a loud hoot from Robert, who was giving off bubble balloons like a figure in a comic strip. He jabbed his finger at a branch of the black tree. There sat a fish three inches long with a body pattern of perfect squares like a tiled floor. After that, I think I would have believed a man who came out of the roof and told me he had seen an octopus wearing a derby hat and smoking a cigar. We have described the checkerboard fish to marine biologists; none have ever heard of anything like it.

During her protracted anchorage at Assumption Reef, *Calypso* became a sort of satellite island and attracted her own finny populace. At dusk each day, schools of two-foot-long milkfish arrived and spiraled around the ship in geometric formations, holding their heads out of the water. The slightest human interference—a shout, a spotlight, or a diver's fin off the ladder—dispersed this timid assemblage of eyes and tiny, upraised mouths.

During our dreary decompression stops 10 feet under *Calypso*, we noted a lone barracuda, about 4 feet long, that skulked on the outskirts, never coming near us. We also saw three dozen remoras that had clamped themselves on the stern quarters 2,000 miles back when we killed their shark hosts. The suckerfish had apparently been living on *Calypso*'s garbage. We inventoried the remoras during stage decompression and learned that one or two of them left the ship each day. We wondered why. When a dozen suckerfish were left, Falco started diving at dawn to see why the remoras were leaving. His prowl was rewarded by something none of us had seen in thousands of hours underwater.

Falco came dripping to the breakfast table. "I saw the barracuda take a remora," he said. "I was a hundred feet away. The barracuda dashed to the stern and picked it off. I went in quickly. The barracuda had cut it in two and swallowed half. It had the other half crosswise in its mouth as it swam away." There it was: *Calypso* was providing bed and breakfast for a barracuda. We broke our truce on killing in the Aldabras. "Get your *arbalete*," I told Falco. He dived with his spear gun and executed the barracuda with a single shot.

There are three disturbing aspects of barracudas—their evil, threatening faces, their disagreeable habit of swimming close to your feet, and their gaudy reputation as man-eaters. The latter is merely an assumption based on the first attribute. Still . . . early in our work at Assumption, I was 60 feet down in the reef, filming close-ups of the guests in a fancy coral hotel. When the reel ran out, I gave the camera to my assistant to carry up while I used the rest of my air on a sightseeing ramble.

I turned away from him and looked at a wall of middle-sized barracudas. I looked up and down and to the sides through my diving mask, which limits vision like horse blinders. The bulkhead of barracudas extended from the ocean floor to the surface. Alone and barehanded, I could not suppress a tremor of panic. We had never paid attention to barracudas, and I had dismissed them in print as being of no danger to divers. Now, in this confrontation, I was not so sure. They might have a mob psychology that would produce a sudden, irreparable act at any moment.

I told myself to stop being frightened and take refuge on the reef. I wheeled. A curtain of barracudas obscured the reef. With a hammering heart, I turned full around. I was encircled by wild animals, revolving deliberately around me, three or four fish thick. I could not see through them. There was no way out. I sank motionless to the bottom of the well, conserving the remainder of my air. The great silver cylinder turned evenly on the axis of my exhalations several times and then unrolled in a curtain of tail fins stroking west in the ocean.

On his first dive at Assumption, Marden encountered a grouper of about 60 pounds with a brownish coat and a pale marbled pattern that changed from time to time. The big fish strolled up to Marden, and he prepared to take its portrait. The grouper nudged the flashbulb bag with its nose. Luis backed away to get a proper focus. The fish followed, showing interest in the shiny parts of the camera. By a series of retreats, Marden finally shot it in focus and swam away to find other fish. The grouper tagged along, nuzzling the photographer and his glittering gadgetry. As Luis lined up on another subject, the big fish interposed itself in the camera field. The diver dodged aside and made his shot. As he detached the used bulb from the reflector, the fish tried to eat it.

After Marden brought up this tale, Delmas and Dumas went down into the grouper's territory with a canvas bag full of chopped meat. The big fish came to them. The divers released some food into the water and the cavernous mouth opened. Giving the appearance of a flock of birds entering a tunnel, the meat scraps vanished into its belly. The underwatermen experimented cautiously with hand feeding, and the big fish plucked meat off their fingertips without harming them. In that first session Dumas and Delmas, using food rewards in various acrobatic situations, taught the grouper several tricks. They named the clever beast Ulysses.

Ulysses became our inseparable friend. He followed us everywhere, sometimes nibbling our fins. After deep dives, when we were decompressing 30 feet down on a weighted and measured cable, the boredom was enlivened by Ulysses' horsing around with us until we went to the ladder. Afterward he would hang around just under the surface, sitting on his tail, like a boy sadly watching his playmates being called in to supper. Ulysses quickly got on to our diving schedule and would be found early in the morning waiting under the ladder for the day's first sortie. He would go bounding down with us for a round of clumsy mischief and meals from the canvas bag.

Ulysses was a close cousin of the *merous* we knew in the Mediterranean. However, after twenty-five years of underwater hunting the merous had been conditioned to distrust man. In the first aqualung days they had come close and stared at us as Ulysses did, but in our home sea spears had ruined the possibility of an intimate association such as this. We had previously met at Aldabra another innocent grouper that could have been Ulysses' twin. It lived in a large black coral tree that we were attempting to remove as a specimen. The fish watched our labor. We got a sling on the tree and heaved it out with *Calypso*'s biggest winch. The grouper nervously accompanied his tree as it slowly ascended. Several times he dropped back to look at where it had been and then climbed up to where it was presently. As his home left the sea, the fish looked more down-in-the-mouth than usual.

Ulysses had refined his home life to a greater degree. We located his apartment, a deep crevice in the coral, which was hardly big enough to contain him but had the security factor of two entrances. The lair was 30 feet down, opening onto a terrace of white sand. The entries were bare and polished from his comings and goings. The place might as well have had his name plate on the door.

When in a good mood—and his emotions were by no means uniform—Ulysses would let any of us caress him and scratch his head. Dumas, partially concealing the meat bag in his hand, stood in midwater and turned at a slow, three-step tempo. Following the bait around, Ulysses joined the dance. When Dumas spun the other way, the fish followed right on the beat. It was done so lightly and rhythmically that we were able to film it as a waltz.

But Ulysses had a temper, too. Sometimes he bungled into camera setups of Marden's or Malle's, and they shoved him away impatiently. Then he would leave, slamming the door behind him. As a matter of fact, when he flounced off, his first tail stroke was so powerful that it made an audible boom, probably caused by cavitation. He also resented us when we forgot to bring him the meat bag. When angry, he would hang 30 feet off, keeping to that distance whether we went toward him or away from him. However, next morning he would be waiting under the diving ladder, his grievances forgotten.

Delmas observed a certain cautious etiquette about feeding Ulysses, for as soon as one lump of meat was out of the bag, that huge gaping mouth flew at it. A grouper has no real teeth, but his mouth and throat have rows of grinders that would not improve the use of your arm if you placed it inside. One morning Ulysses made a sly and rapid dash for the sack, tore it out of Delmas' hand, and swallowed it whole. He marched brazenly away, well aware that there was no more food forthcoming.

The next morning there was no Ulysses under the ladder. Down in our studio he did not appear. In the afternoon divers spread out to look for him. We found him lying on the sand in front of his den. His gills were pulsing at an unreasonable rate like the panting of a sick man. He had no interest in us. On the following morning he was still in bed with a severe case of indigestion caused by the stolen bag. I consulted Dr. Martin-Laval, who said Ulysses was in danger of a fatal intestinal obstruction. He advised us to keep him under observation. On the third day, we found the fish fallen flat on his side, seemingly critically ill. I went up and asked the doctor to do something. Martin-Laval was confronted with his most unusual case. Since he could not bring the fish to his surgery, he prepared to operate in the patient's bedroom. He gathered anesthetics, knives, surgical clips, and catgut and needle to suture the opening after he had removed the bag from Ulysses' tortured interior. The surgeon briefed three divers to act as his assistants. It was sundown before the preparations were in hand, and we went to sleep hoping that Ulysses would last through the night.

At first light, a reconnaissance team plunged. Ulysses was gone from his veranda. The divers roamed about, looking for him. Falco felt somebody pulling at his back harness. It was Ulysses, announcing that everything was okay. He was gay and hungry. He had managed to eliminate the meat sack.

Reluctantly we decided that *Calypso* could not postpone her trip to Aldabra forever, so we took four days off to journey to the big atoll. Moving out of the bay, we came upon a boat containing one of the four inhabitants of Assumption Island. He held up an enormous grouper. It was a 60-pounder, undoubtedly Ulysses. Our passage to Aldabra was full of mourning and disgust. We said a lot at table about the disastrous influence of man on nature. Our species were cursed! Ulysses would never have grown so large had he not had an instinctive aversion to hooks, but we had accustomed him to association with man—we had baited him with finger morsels and led him to bite the fatal hook.

We returned to Assumption in a different mood from the joyful day of discovery. With Ulysses gone, the reef wonderland would not be the same. While I was maneuvering *Calypso* toward the anchorage, Falco could not contain his impatience. He jumped overboard with mask and fins and swam toward the fabled reef. Then his fins shot into the air and down he went. He popped back, leaping out of the water like a hysterical porpoise. "Ulysses is alive!" Falco bellowed. As soon as the diving ladder was down, our friend was there waiting for the fun to resume.

Although Ulysses was a loner, there were two slightly smaller groupers living a hundred feet from him on either side. They were much less interested in men. As we came to know the region, we observed that none of the three would venture into each other's territory. They were chieftains of three principalities. When we swam into the flanking domains, Ulysses would stop at the border and accompany us no further. Just across the invisible boundary the other lord would be on patrol. We never witnessed a border fight but sensed that they occurred. Observance of property rights was relaxed for two other smaller groupers that traveled freely across the frontiers. Their attitude toward divers was unpredictable. They were usually aggressive, but at other times seemed timid. We were fairly sure that they were females. Once we found them close to Ulysses, weaving in a suggestive way, all three fishes turned completely white.

We experimented with feeding other denizens of the reef, and all responded heartily. We swam along, distributing chopped meat from a bag in the manner of a peasant sowing grain. This attracted fish by the thousands—especially pretty yellow snappers, which swept along at our heels pecking the manna from heaven. Watching us feed them put Ulysses in a towering rage. He would crash into the sack, bite our fins, tug on our bathing trunks, and whip his big tail to scatter the little ones.

We wanted to film this golden host following a manfish across the reef, but Ulysses kept breaking it up. He would not get out of the scene and often bumped the camera or the flood lamps. Falco thought of a way to get rid of him without banging his snout and injuring his *amour-propre*. We assembled the antishark cage and dropped it to the bottom. Ulysses supervised the placing of the yellow cage and the opening of the door. Delmas waved his feeding arm toward the opening and the fish swam in. The door clanked shut, and Ulysses was in protective custody.

As a sort of object lesson, Delmas fed a rally of snappers just outside the bars while Ulysses glowered. But the caterer did not have the heart to torture his friend more and decided that Ulysses should have a special treat while he was in jail. This was the same day that Falco killed the barracuda that had been feeding on the remoras. We wondered whether Ulysses would care for a 20-pound barracuda, which was as long as he was, although sticklike by comparison. We took the still-bleeding marauder down to the cage and poked the head of the long fish through the bars. Without hesitation Ulysses gulped in more than half the barracuda's body, leaving the tail sticking from his mouth. The grouper seemed to regard this as nothing out of the ordinary and remained for hours with the barracuda protruding from his mouth. When we left for the night, there was still about a third of the barracuda visible. In the morning it was gone. We were puzzled over how Ulysses managed it. The barracuda was stiff as a broomstick and certainly could not have been doubled up in the stomach. The head must have been jammed right into the pit of Ulysses' gut. Apparently the grouper simply turned on his gastric juices to melt away the front end, bones and all, and ingested the rest when he had made room for it.

Ulysses was caged for three days while we completed the film. When we opened the jail door, the grouper watched with interest but made no move to depart. In vain did Delmas wave his magic arm. Apparently our friend, considering the abundant food provided in the cage, preferred to stay there. Falco went in with him and pushed him through the door. Ulysses swam off in a sulk, at a much slower pace than usual. He was fat and out of shape.

After five weeks at the reef, cook Hanen warned me that we were running low on food. He refused to let Delmas and Dumas have any more meat to feed the fishes, so they turned to bootlegging Ulysses' daily fare. The twosome stretched this out by diving for tridacnas and mincing the clam meat in with the kitchen scraps. There were some curious looks from hungry deckhands who passed the kitchen and saw two madmen chopping up delicious protein to give to fish. The divers were exhausted and wobbling with reef fever, but nobody wanted to leave. We still had a week's rationed supply of fresh water.

Six days afterward, Hanen told me he had no meat left. Since we were about to leave, I decided we should make a decent final meal. I asked Delmas to go down and spear a fat grouper, and I accompanied him. So did Ulysses. It was like hunting with a retriever dog. Delmas selected a black grouper and triggered his spear gun. What happened then came so fast that it took a moment to sort it out. Virtually synchronized with the flight of the spear, Ulysses hit the fish, and then we saw its tail and the four-foot harpoon protruding from his mouth. Delmas placed his foot against Ulysses' head and heaved hard to extract the spear. This gave the grouper more room to accommodate the catch, and he swallowed it all except the tip of the tail.

We returned to *Calypso* and told the hungry mob that our pet had eaten their dinner. Delmas and I were much impressed by Ulysses' reflexes. For weeks he had followed us about at a lumbering gait, with only a hint of his power and speed when he cracked his tail whip or when he stole the meat bag. Now he had showed us how sharp he was the first time another creature got into trouble along the reef. This pointed out one of the main laws of our jungle. To catch a healthy fish in a three-dimensional world was a difficult task, but there was no mercy for any kind of disabled individual.

By the close of our sixth week at Assumption Reef, we were a bunch of rickety scarecrows, breaking into teeth-chattering bouts of Tontonitis, and covered with pious sores. The eye still came alight with pleasure at the thought of the next dive, but there was a glint of dementia in it. The game was up. We had to leave. "Let's take Ulysses with us," said Delmas.

The idea was met with enthusiasm. The bosun planned a tarpaulin-lined pool on the afterdeck. However, I had to oppose the notion. In France, Ulysses either would face life imprisonment in an aquarium or would have to be liberated in the sea. He was probably not adapted for colder water. On top of that he was so friendly that the first spearman he met would have an easy kill. As the capstan rattled, we dived for the last time and waved good-bye to our friend.

Four years later, after Ulysses had become a movie star in our film *The Silent World,* a boat sailing around the world made a special call at Assumption Bay and sent divers down to look for the tame grouper. The circumnavigators reported, "Ulysses is doing fine. He was easy to recognize. He swam up immediately to the divers." Perhaps we will go back someday and see him again. He's a fish worth going halfway round the earth to meet.

Part 4

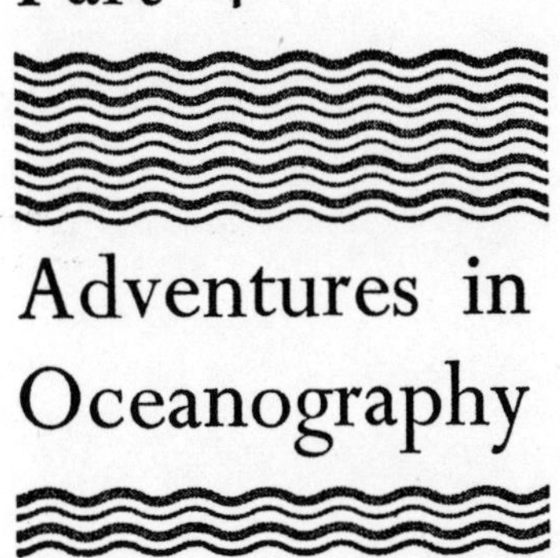

Adventures in Oceanography

The Shape of the Sea

by
Arthur C. Clarke

In the not too distant past, having little actual knowledge, man conceived of the ocean bottom as a flat and featureless plain, devoid of any vestige of plant or animal life, eternally dark and still. With greater knowledge, we have been forced to revise every aspect of this imaginary picture. Far from being flat and featureless, the bottom is in places even more rugged than the Himalayas. Animal life has been observed at far greater depths than we had supposed possible. Turbidity currents, mixtures of earth and mud or sand, disturb the undersea placidity with the power of landslides. Even the eternal darkness is lit by intermittent flashes of light emitted by marine animals. Our information comes from a variety of sources. We have seen how Piccard observed the deepest chasm in the ocean. Echo sounders help us draw accurate topographic maps. Specially equipped ships, carrying scientists trained in every aspect of oceanography, sail the seven seas. At last we begin to have an accurate picture of the shape of the sea and the history of the earth that lies buried beneath the sea. Arthur C. Clarke tells something of what we have learned.

ALTHOUGH men have been sailing the seas for at least five thousand years, it was only during the nineteenth century that they discovered the true size and shape of the oceans. The maps showed that there was much more sea than land—about three-quarters of the earth is covered with water—but how deep that water was no one knew. Only near the shore was it possible to reach bottom with a sounding line—a heavy weight or lead tied to the end of a rope. When they tried this in the open sea, hundreds of miles from the nearest land, the old-time sailors failed to touch the bottom. Their lines were too short, and anyway they weren't particularly interested. As long as the water was deep enough to sail in—that was the only thing that mattered to them. From their point of view it was all the same whether the ocean was one mile or a hundred miles deep. What practical importance was it to anyone to know how far down the sea bed was? Only a few long-haired scientists were interested in such things.

And then, just over a hundred years ago, the depths

of the sea suddenly became of very great importance to all civilized countries. The invention of the electric telegraph, early in the nineteenth century, made it possible to send messages thousands of miles in a few seconds between any two points where wires could be laid. Naturally, it was not long before men started to think about laying a cable across the Atlantic, so that Europe and America could talk to each other with the speed of electricity instead of having to wait weeks for ships to make the crossing. But before a transatlantic cable could be laid it was necessary to know the depth of the Atlantic, and also the nature of its bed. And so in the 1850's the first real deep-sea surveys were carried out by the British and American navies, along a line that joined Newfoundland and Ireland.

It took hours to make each measurement, for the ship had to be stopped, the heavily weighted line lowered to the bottom, and then the two or three miles of rope hauled up again. But slowly the picture of the Atlantic seabed built up on the charts—the outlines of hills and valleys that no man had ever seen, the shapes of sunken mountains rising from great plains of mud that had gathered for a million years. Because the depth measurements, or soundings, took so long to make, there were a good many miles between each one, and so the map of the seabed was very far from being complete. In fact, it was full of gaps, yet it was still a great achievement. The scientists and naval officers who carried out these early surveys were rather like men floating high across the United States in a balloon, trying—in complete darkness—to discover the shape of the land beneath them by letting down a weight on a piece of string. Such a slow and crude method of measurement would give fairly good results over the flat states of the Midwest, but it could give only a very rough picture of the Rockies. It might even miss completely something as large as the Grand Canyon.

We should not be surprised, therefore, that the first surveys of the North Atlantic showed the seabed to be much smoother and flatter than it really is. Perhaps this was a good thing. If the scientists of the 1850's had known all its ups and downs, they would have been so discouraged that they might not have tried to lay a cable across it. According to their measurements, most of the North Atlantic seabed was a fairly level plain (christened Telegraph Plateau) about two miles down, and at no point was the ocean more than two and a half miles deep.

As we shall see later, the true picture is much more complicated, and how this was discovered is a fascinating example of the way in which modern science has allowed us to learn things about the deep sea which could never have been guessed when our grandparents were children. The invention that allows us to map the bed of the ocean with such speed and accuracy that we can almost see it is the echo sounder.

The principle of the echo sounder is extremely simple, and you can demonstrate it yourself quite easily if you stand about 50 feet away from a high wall or a tall building. (The best place to try the experiment is in a narrow, dead-end street, with walls all around you.) If you clap your hands or stamp your feet you'll hear an echo coming back a fraction of a second later, faint but clear. It is the noise you made returning to you after being reflected from the far wall. There may be several echoes from walls at different distances.

Let's suppose that you hear the main echo just a tenth of a second after you've made the noise. Sound moves through the air at about a thousand feet a second (the speed varies with the temperature, but let's not worry about that at the moment). So your echo must have traveled 100 feet, and this means that the wall must be 50 feet away—since the sound has to make the round trip there and back.

The idea of using underwater sounds to get echoes from the seabed, and so to measure its depth, now seems very obvious and elementary, but not until 1920 was it put into practice. The modern echo sounder employs a kind of loudspeaker attached to the hull of the ship below the water line, and every few seconds this shoots a sudden, high-pitched shriek down toward the seabed. The returning echo is picked up by a microphone, and appears as a spot on a moving chart or on a screen like that of a TV set. And so, as the ship sails along, the echo sounder can draw a continuous picture of the seabed below it—a picture so accurate that it will show wrecks and even schools of fish.

What a contrast to the old days when a ship had to stay fixed for hours to make a single sounding! Now it takes only seconds, and the ship can travel at full speed.

The echo sounder is a fine example of the way in which a new invention—often quite a simple one—can revolutionize some branch of science. It happened in astronomy when the first telescope was built, and in biology when the microscope was invented. In fact, almost all our knowledge of the deep sea has been gained by the use of special instruments of some kind or other, and more are being built all the time. But we shall need many, many more before we can understand all the mysteries of the ocean.

Some of those mysteries concern the shape of the seabed, now revealed to us in detail by the echo sounder—although there are still enormous areas uncharted, especially in the Pacific. Perhaps the best way to picture the floor of the ocean is to imagine that you are driving out from land in a kind of submarine tank that can crawl along the seabed. Such vehicles have been built, although none that can go as deep as we shall pretend. We'll also assume that we can see as far underwater as we can on land, so that we can look at the hills and valleys around us. In actual fact, you can seldom see more than a hundred feet underwater, and visibility is usually very much poorer than this. A diver often considers himself lucky when he can see 10 feet.

Well, here we go! The water gurgles around the

conning tower as we sink beneath the waves. Ahead lies an immense plain of sand and mud, with occasional rocks and boulders scattered across it—not to mention dozens of wrecks in various stages of decay. We are on the edge of the continental shelf, the wide, gently sloping platform that surrounds most of the world's major land masses. You will have to look very closely to see that it is sloping at all. Our submarine tank may have to travel miles out from land before the water reaches a depth of 500 feet. On the average, the continental shelf is about thirty miles wide, although in places like the Grand Banks of Newfoundland, it stretches for several hundred miles.

But at last the shelf comes to an end. Fairly suddenly, the seabed starts to angle downward. We have entered the zone known as the slope, and it is like driving down a very gentle hill. Mile after mile we descend while the depth of the water mounts above us. Now we must measure our distance to the surface not in hundreds, but in thousands, of feet. We passed the 5,000-foot line long ago. Now we are at 10,000 feet—almost two miles down. The descent, however, is no longer so rapid; the slope is flattening out. Presently we are moving once more across a level plain which stretches for hundreds of miles ahead of us. We have reached the abyss, the true floor of the ocean.

Continental shelf, slope, abyss—these are the three main regions into which the ocean is divided. On the average, the abyss is about two and a half miles down

—but this figure is nothing like the greatest depth in the sea, for the journey I have described was a very smooth and uneventful one. It completely missed the strangest and most spectacular features of the sea bed.

If we had started out to sea in some parts of the world—off the mouth of the Hudson River, for example—we would have found that both the continental shelf and the slope beyond it were torn and gashed by enormous valleys or chasms, some of them 100 miles long and 10 or 20 miles wide. These sunken canyons, greater than any on the dry land, would be awe-inspiring sights if they were visible to the eye; but we know them only through the readings of the echo sounder. Some of them are mightier than the Grand Canyon, which is perhaps the most impressive spectacle on the surface of the earth.

Now here is a major mystery. The Grand Canyon was formed by the action of the Colorado River slowly carving away the rock, century by century. The river is still doing its work, as anyone can see who has looked down into the canyon and watched the muddy waters moving far below. But these great canyons in the sea—how were *they* formed? Some of them are a mile deep, and it's hard to imagine rivers flowing at the bottom of the sea!

Yet there are rivers in the sea, some of them bigger than the Mississippi. One theory is that great submarine currents carved these gorges leading down to the ocean deeps. Another is that the level of the sea has risen so far—or the land has dropped so much—

that these regions of the seabed were once dry land through which some ancestor of the Colorado River flowed millions of years ago. It is almost impossible to imagine such vast upheavals of land and sea. If they are still going on, it may mean that one day the Grand Canyon will be a mile below water, perplexing the scientists of the far future.

The mysterious canyons belong to the edges of the continents, but further out in the open sea are much deeper gorges. In these trenches, as they are called, are the greatest of all ocean depths. Soundings of over 36,000 feet have been made in the Pacific, off the Marianas. If Mount Everest were sunk in the Marianas Trench, its summit would still be a mile below sea level.

The ocean contains mountains as well as valleys. Some of these mountains have been known since the earliest times, for their peaks rise above the water to form islands such as the Azores. But many more are completely submerged and have been discovered only recently. The greatest mountain range on earth is not on any of the continents but halfway between America and Europe. For 7,000 miles the Atlantic Ridge runs southward from Iceland almost to the Antarctic Circle, spanning a third of the circumference of the globe. In places it soars two miles above the seabed—yet even then it misses the surface by a mile.

During the war a scientist, who also happened to be the commanding officer of a United States Navy transport, discovered a new type of undersea mountain recorded on the charts of his echo sounder. In many parts of the Pacific, isolated flat-topped mountains rise abruptly from the sea bed—sunken mesas as much as a mile below the surface. Samples dredged from the tops of these hidden plateaus show that they are the stumps of mountains that towered above the sea, perhaps a hundred million years ago. The rains and the waves of centuries wore them down to sea level, thus producing their flat tops. And then, quite suddenly (as time is measured by the geologists) they sank into the depths of the Pacific where they remain to this day as fossil mountains from the Age of Reptiles, holding unknown secrets from the past.

The ocean bed, therefore, contains even more varied scenery than the dry land; its mountain ranges are longer, its canyons wider and deeper than any on the continents. It will be many years before we have mapped it completely—and many more before we have explored it in detail, for the sheer volume of the sea is almost beyond human imagination. It does not convey much to say that the oceans contain 300 million cubic miles of water, but perhaps this fact will help you to get this enormous figure into perspective: There is enough water in the sea to provide every man, woman and child on earth with a private swimming pool a mile long, a mile wide—and 500 feet deep.

And, of course, the sea is not merely plain water. It is a world of life and energy, sometimes calm and peaceful, sometimes shaken by storms and blasted by submarine volcanoes. Even down in the abyss, two or three miles below the waves, the water is not wholly still, but moves in sluggish currents that ripple the deep-sea muds and oozes. Deeper yet, in the great trenches six miles from the last light of the sun, one might expect to find eternal calm. But this is not so, for the trenches are the birthplace of earthquakes which may send tidal waves spreading death and destruction for thousands of miles.

Enormous, wonderful and even terrifying is the strange world waiting for us beneath the waves.

The history of the world lies buried at the bottom of the sea. The ocean bed is a book which we are just beginning to read—or, rather, to decipher, for it is written in a strange language, and many of its myriad pages are missing. Others are still being written, carrying a record of our present age which, perhaps, scientists from distant worlds may read a million years from now.

The pages of this book are made of rather dull substances—muds and oozes. In this case, however, they are anything but dull, for they tell of sunken continents, of volcanic eruptions which must have darkened the skies of earth, of mighty ice fields grinding down from the poles, and of the beginning of life itself upon our planet.

To us, the dry land with its hills and mountains seems eternal, but every drop of rain that returns to the sea takes with it some of the solid earth beneath our feet. Century by century, even the mightiest mountain ranges are worn away. The Rockies and Himalayas that we know are mere ghosts of their former selves, and one day they will have disappeared completely.

The sediment swept out to sea forms vast layers of mud over the continental shelves, but the deeper parts of the ocean are covered with a different kind of carpet. This is formed by the skeletons, made of lime or silica, of trillions upon trillions of tiny plankton plants and animals raining down eternally from the watery heights above. Although these creatures are almost invisibly small, they exist in such countless numbers that their remains have built up mile-thick layers of ooze or clay on the seabed. When this ooze hardens, it becomes chalk or limestone, so every hill or cliff made of these rocks was formed at the bottom of the sea.

Rachel Carson, in her famous book, *The Sea Around Us*, called this perpetual downward drift of tiny skeletons "the long snowfall," and the phrase gives a good mental picture of the steadily thickening carpet covering the bottoms of all the oceans of the world. The empty shells and skeletons are also as beautifully and intricately fashioned as any snowflakes. Unlike snowflakes, however, they are almost eternal. When they have settled to the seabed, they can there remain for a thousand million years.

In some parts of the Atlantic the carpet of sediment

is more than two miles thick. It takes several thousand years to build up a layer only one inch deep, so this means that the "long snowfall" has lasted at least 500 million years. It also means that the Atlantic has been an ocean for all this length of time. By comparison, most continents and mountain ranges are creations of yesterday.

During the last twenty years scientists have devoted much effort to obtaining samples of this deep-sea carpet. Coring devices have been invented which can punch holes in the sea bed and bring up continuous tubes of sediment as much as 100 feet in length. When the value of the ships, equipment, and man power involved in getting them is added up, these cores have probably cost their weight in gold. They are worth it, for they open a door into the unknown past.

When a tree trunk is sawed through, you can see that it is built up layer by layer in concentric rings, each ring representing the growth in one year. For this reason, it is a simple matter to find the age of a tree merely by counting rings. The experts, however, can do much more than this. Seasons of drought or of heavy rainfall thousands of years ago can be pinpointed by the thickness of the rings. In a bad year, there is scarcely any growth; in a good one, the tree puts on an extra-thick layer.

Something similar happens at the bottom of the sea, except that here the time scale is measured in centuries instead of years. A geologist can work along a core punched from the ocean bed, and can watch the coming and going of the Ice Ages. At one level, for example, there will be the skeletons of creatures that live only in tropical seas. A few inches away—that is, ten or twenty thousand years further back in the past—the skeletons are those of cold-water animals. And here there may be pebbles and grits that can only have come from the land. How did they reach this point, a thousand miles from the nearest shore? Icebergs carried them here when they calved off the glaciers covering the frozen continents; as they melted, they dumped these souvenirs from distant lands.

By such patient detective work, the geologists can study climatic changes that occurred before the first man walked the earth. And recently they have been able to do something even more marvelous. They have been able to measure the actual temperature of the ocean hundreds of thousands of years ago. When you stop to think about it, such a feat seems absolutely incredible. Without a time machine, there would seem to be no way of going back into the past and dipping a thermometer into some primeval sea.

This miraculous piece of scientific detection has been made possible by a very delicate chemical analysis of certain shells taken from the deep-sea cores. The rate at which shells absorb elements from the sea water around them depends upon the temperature, just as the rate of growth of tree rings depends upon the rainfall. And so it is now possible to draw a graph of the rise and fall of the thermometer in seas that rolled a million years ago.

And here is another secret of the past which has been wrested from the clay and ooze of the seabed: Which way did the compass point in 500,000 B.C.? A few years ago, no one would have dreamed that such a question could ever be answered. But today, by studying the direction in which various magnetic substances have come to point as they drifted to the sea bed, we are able to study the movement of the earth's magnetic poles, thousands of years before the compass was invented—or there were any men to use it.

It may not sound very romantic to call the sea a cosmic garbage dump, but the debris of land, air, and even space is continually drifting down into its depths. At this moment, we are contributing to it in no small way. Every diver has come across empty bottles and cans, burned out electric bulbs, lost anchors, old boots—the list is endless and includes practically every object that man has ever made. But long before men sailed the ocean, nature was dumping her rubbish into the waves, and we have been able to learn a great deal from the trash of centuries that has gathered on the sea bed. One recent discovery which may be of extreme importance—although its exact meaning is still unknown—is that huge areas of the Pacific and Atlantic are covered with layers of volcanic ash. Judging from its depth in the sediment, this ash was deposited about seventy thousand years ago. Some titanic eruption must have taken place then, perhaps one violent enough to have produced major changes in the geography of the earth.

Just now we mentioned debris from space—yes, that lies on the seabed, although in very minute quantities. Meteors are continually raining down upon our planet, and most of them fall into the sea. So occasionally tiny globules of meteor dust are discovered in some marine sediments. There may be many very large meteors in the sea as well, but we have not yet found them.

There must be some areas of the ocean where there are no currents or earthquakes to disturb the eternal submarine snowfall, and where the entire history of the last few billion years lies in layer upon layer waiting to be read, with all the pages intact and in their correct order. On land, the geological record is never complete, for the rocks which carry the messages of the past are themselves being continually worn away, and are often broken or overturned by the movements of the continents. Getting at that sunken history book, two or three miles below the surface, is one of the greatest tasks facing the oceanographers.

Today's hundred-foot cores merely scratch the surface of the deep-sea sediment. They span only a million years of its history. How can we obtain a sample through its entire thickness which may be as much as 12,000 feet? This is still an unsolved problem in underwater engineering, but a daring attempt to do this—and more—is now being planned by scientists in the United States and the Soviet Union.

We have successfully drilled oil wells on the sea bed from boats anchored offshore. It is believed that the same technique can be used to drill holes not only through the sediments on the ocean bed, but also clear through the outer crust of the earth itself.

During the next few years you are going to hear a good deal about this plan to drill a hole through the sea bed into the earth's interior. It will cost as much as a space satellite, and will lead to discoveries of equal importance, because for the first time it will give us samples of the unknown stuff of which our planet is made. And if it also provides the geologists with a complete section through the billion or more years of sediment on the ocean bed, it will allow them to look back into time, almost as dramatically as the satellites have enabled the astronomers to look out into space.

Just as there are layers in the sky, like the famous Heaviside Layer which reflects radio waves, and the recently discovered Van Allen radiation belts, so there are layers of various kinds within the earth. They were first detected by a study of earthquake records, for earthquakes send vibrations racing back and forth inside the solid body of our globe, and by measuring their time of arrival, scientists have been able to construct a kind of X-ray picture of the earth.

In this way, a Yugoslavian scientist named Mohorivicic discovered a dividing layer—or discontinuity—between the familiar rocks which make up the outer crust of our planet and the denser material which extends all the way to the earth's core, some two thousand miles down. Since it takes several seconds' hard work to say "Mohorivicic discontinuity," even when you know how, the abbreviation Moho is universally used for this layer.

The Moho is not at the same depth everywhere. Under the land, it is about 20 miles down—far deeper than any well can be drilled, for the record at the moment is only 5 miles. But under the sea, it is much closer to us, sometimes only 3 miles below the ocean bed, or a total of 6 miles down from sea level. It is not surprising, therefore, that scientists are excited at the idea of using the new underwater drilling techniques to break through to the earth's interior, so tantalizingly close at hand.

Let us stop to think what this may mean. As the long tubes of densely packed sediment are brought up to the surface, we shall be boring back through the ages, just as the archaeologists who excavated Troy peeled away the centuries, layer by layer, to find that one city had been built upon another. But Troy was only a moment ago. We may be going back a million times further into the unknown past. The first cores will repeat the story of the Ice Ages that we have already traced, and for a while we will be drilling our way through familiar eras of time. Every foot of the core will represent perhaps fifty thousand years of prehistory, and soon the head of the drill will be passing through layers that settled to the bed of the ocean when the great reptiles ruled the earth.

Yet even that is not so long ago, in the immense

vistas of geological time. The last of the dinosaurs perished some 60 million years ago, and the earth may be a hundred times as old as this. As the drill works its way backward into the records of the rocks, the fragments of shells and skeletons it brings up will belong to ever more primitive creatures—perhaps creatures so close to the beginning of life that we have found no trace of them on land. And at some point, corresponding to a time about a billion years ago, there will be a change in the material brought up. It will no longer contain fragments of once-living creatures, for the drill will have gone past the moment when life appeared on earth. We will be looking at our world as it was before a single blade of grass waved on land, or a single primitive jellyfish drifted in the sea.

Like the reader of a mystery story who has turned most of the pages of the book and is now rushing headlong toward its ending, we, too, will be about to unravel a secret. It will be one of the greatest of all secrets, that of life itself, and the way it began on earth.

Below this level there will be only the record of the winds and rains and volcanoes as they carved and molded the empty earth, preparing it for the dramas still to come. When our questing drills reach this depth, they will enter a world we would not recognize. They may reach the original surface of our planet, as it was in the days when it was formed. And so we will have traveled back in time not only to the coming of life, but beyond that to the origin of the earth.

CATASTROPHIC WAVES FROM THE SEA

by

Francis P. Shepard

Only on rare occasions can a qualified student observe the cataclysmic movements of earth and sea in which he is expert. We have learned to recognize certain preliminary signals that herald volcanic eruptions or earthquakes, but the exact time of actual happening is usually unpredictable. For these reasons, the chapter below is one of the most interesting in the literature of oceanography. Francis P. Shepard, of the Scripps Institute of Oceanography at La Jolla, California, is a noted expert on ocean waves and currents. His study of the destructive effects of such movements is world famous, and he has been instrumental in setting up early-warning systems that have saved thousands of lives. Some of his knowledge has been dearly bought, as witness this description of the catastrophic tidal wave which engulfed a Hawaiian shore in 1946 and which he personally observed. His account is included in this book of undersea adventures because the origins of such waves lie hidden beneath the ocean floor. Undersea earthquakes and landslides cause disturbances in the waters above them, and the shock of these disturbances, sometimes traveling tens of thousands of miles, wreaks havoc on unsuspecting victims, as well as on those who, having been forewarned, choose to disregard the lessons that science teaches.

THE TERM *tidal wave* has had an ominous sound in Hawaii since April 1, 1946. My own experience on that day may serve to introduce the discussion of tidal waves, or tsunamis. At that time my wife and I were living in a rented cottage at Kawela Bay on northern Oahu. On the previous day, a Sunday, the beaches and reefs were swarming with people and the cottages alive with activity. Fortunately, almost everybody left to go back to Honolulu that night. Early the next morning we were sleeping peacefully when we were awakened by a loud hissing sound, which sounded for all the world as if dozens of locomotives were blowing off steam directly outside our house. Puzzled, we jumped up and rushed to the front window. Where there had been a beach previously, we saw nothing but boiling water, which was sweeping over the 10-foot top of the beach ridge and coming directly at the house. I rushed and grabbed my camera, forgetting such incidentals as clothes, glasses, watch, and pocket-book. As I opened the door I noticed with some regret that the water was not advancing any farther but, instead, was retreating rapidly down the slope.

By that time I was conscious of the fact that we might be experiencing a tsunami. My suspicions became confirmed as the water moved swiftly seaward, and the sea level dropped a score of feet, leaving the coral reefs in front of the house exposed to view. Fish were flapping and jumping up and down where they had been stranded by the retreating waves. Quickly taking a couple of photographs, in my confusion I accidentally made a double exposure of the bare reef. Trying to show my erudition, I said to my wife, "There will be another wave, but it won't be as exciting as the one that awakened us. Too bad I couldn't get a photograph of the first one."

Was I mistaken? In a few minutes as I stood at the edge of the beach ridge in front of the house, I could see the water beginning to rise and swell up around the outer edges of the exposed reef; it built higher and higher and then came racing forward with amazing velocity. "Now," I said, "here is a good chance for a picture." I took one, but my hand was rather unsteady that time. As the water continued to advance I shot another one, fortunately a little better. As it piled up in front of me, I began to wonder whether this wave was really going to be smaller than the preceding one. I called to my wife to run to the back of the house for protection, but she had already started, and I followed her just in time. As I looked back I saw the water surging over the spot where I had been standing a moment before. Suddenly we heard the terrible smashing of glass at the front of the house. The refrigerator passed us on the left side moving upright out into the cane field. On the right came a wall of water sweeping toward us down the road that was our escape route from the area. We were also startled to see that there was nothing but kindling wood left of what had been the nearby house to the east. Finally, the water stopped coming on and we were left on a small island, protected by the undamaged portion of the house, which, thanks to its good construction and to the protecting ironwood trees, still withstood the blows. The water had rushed on into the cane field and spent its fury.

My confidence about the waves getting smaller was rapidly vanishing. Having noted that there was a fair interval before the second invasion (actually fifteen minutes as we found out later), we started running along the emerging beach ridge in the only direction in which we could get to the slightly elevated main road. As we ran, we found some very wet and frightened Hawaiian women standing wringing their hands and wondering what to do. With difficulty we persuaded them to come with us along the ridge to a place where there was a break in the cane field. As we hurried through this break, another huge wave came rolling in over the reef and broke with shuddering force against the small escarpment at the top of the beach. Then, rising as a monstrous wall of water, it swept on after us, flattening the cane field with a terrifying sound. We reached the comparative safety of the elevated road just ahead of the wave.

There, in a motley array of costumes, various other refugees were gathered. One couple had been cooking their breakfast when all of a sudden the first wave came in, lifted their house right off its foundation, and carried it several hundred feet into the cane field where it set it down so gently that their breakfast just kept right on cooking. Needless to say, they did not stay to enjoy the meal. Another couple had escaped with difficulty from their collapsing house.

We walked along the road until we could see nearby Kawela Bay, and from there we watched several more waves roar onto the shore. They came with a steep front like the tidal bore that I had seen move up the Bay of Fundy at Moncton, New Brunswick, and up the channels on the tide flat at Mont-Saint-Michel in Normandy. We could see various ruined houses, some of them completely demolished. One house had been thrown into a pond right on top of another. Another was still floating out in the bay.

Finally, after about six waves had moved in, each one apparently getting progressively weaker, I decided I had better go back and see what I could rescue from what was left of the house where we had been living. After all, we were in scanty attire and required clothes. I had just reached the door when I became conscious that a very powerful mass of water was bearing down on the place. This time there simply was no island in back of the house during the height of the wave. I rushed to a nearby tree and climbed it as fast as possible and then hung on for dear life as I swayed back and forth under the impact of the wave. Like the others, this wave soon subsided, and the series of waves that followed were all minor in comparison.

After the excitement was over, we found half of the house still standing and began picking up our belongings. I chased all over the cane fields trying to find books and notes that had been strewn there by the angry waves. We did, finally, discover our glasses undamaged, buried deep in the sand and debris covering the floor. My waterproof wristwatch was found under the house by the owner a week later.

"Well," I thought, "you're a pretty poor oceanographer not to know that tsunamis increase in size with each new wave." As soon as possible I began to look over the literature, and I felt a little better when I could not find any information to the effect that successive waves increase in size, and yet what could be a more important point to remember? You can be sure that since then those of us who have investigated these waves in the Hawaiian Islands have stressed this danger, and I was most happy to find recently at a local island store a tidal-wave warning that emphasized the crescendo to be anticipated in future disasters. Nowadays, also, there are tidal-wave warning alarms that send out alerts either when reports of earthquakes under the ocean indicate dangerous possibilities, or when early waves arrive at other islands along the general route, or when the tide begins to fluctuate in an abnormal fashion. The importance of these warnings can be seen when it is noted that most of the 159 people who were lost during the 1946 tsunami could have saved their lives by running from the scene to higher ground when the waves first began. The Hawaiians are early risers, and being always attuned to the varying moods of the ocean, almost everyone was conscious of a sudden diminution of the noise of the breakers when the sea withdrew. Most people ran to see the strange sight of the reefs being laid bare, and many went out on the reefs to pick up the stranded fish. The 1957 tsunami was almost as destructive to property in Hawaii as that of 1946, but thanks to the warning system no lives were lost. I was shocked to learn that another house in which I had vacationed was destroyed by the 1957 waves.

The meaning of the Japanese word *tunami* (pronounced *tsunami* and hence written that way) is "large waves in harbors," a good name, as it takes a disturbance of this kind to produce large waves in sheltered bays. The tsunamis certainly do not have anything to do with the tide, although the approach of the waves on an open coast where there are no reefs looks like a rapid rise of the tide, hence tidal wave.

Most tsunamis apparently have their origin in the great sea trenches that surround the margin of the

Pacific Ocean. Fortunately for those who live on the west coast of the United States, there are no deep trenches in this section, which is perhaps the reason no appreciable tsunami has been observed along the California coast. Almost all tsunamis are preceded by world-shaking earthquakes, in which all seismograph stations have recorded the earth tremors from the disturbance. It seems likely that the waves are caused by faulting, a sudden dropping or lifting of a segment of the ocean bottom, which results in a displacement of large amounts of water. An alternative explanation is that huge submarine landslides produce the waves, although there is no good confirmation of this idea, and all tsunamis except those caused by volcanic eruptions have followed large earthquakes. If the ocean bottom drops, the surface waters are sucked into the hole, and when the water flowing from either side comes together, the surface of the water rises and waves move out in all directions under the force of gravity. Alternatively, if the bottom rises, the water is lifted and moves outward.

The waves are most violent in their effect in a direction at right angles to the fault. Since the Aleutian Trench, south of the islands of that name, runs east and west, movement along the faults that bound the trench produce waves that are most significant to the north and south, as were those of 1946 and 1957. Almost no one lives along the south exposed side of the Aleutian Islands, so that little damage has resulted in that area, although in 1946 the water rose at Scotch

Cap on Unimak Island to over 100 feet, destroying a lighthouse and flowing over a 100-foot terrace. The Hawaiian Island group, more than 2,000 miles to the south, had waves that washed up to a maximum height of 57 feet, as far as we were able to determine. Fortunately, in most places it did not rise nearly as high as that.

Tsunamis move at an enormous speed in the open ocean, averaging about 450 miles an hour. This varies directly with the depth of the water, because these waves, unlike wind waves, have very long periods, commonly fifteen minutes, and have distances of as much as 100 miles between crests. Their height in the open ocean is so small, however, that they may have no erosive effect on the deep-sea floor. It is only along a coast that they become destructive.

The waves took about four hours to reach Hawaiian shores after the Aleutian earthquake of 1946. As the waves came into shallow water, they were greatly slowed down, so that they advanced at a rate of only about 15 miles an hour as they approached the coast. As their energy became confined to shallow water, they grew in height. The exposed coasts on the north of the Hawaiian Islands had large waves, whereas small heights were observed on the protected south side of the islands.

The investigations that followed the tsunami resulted in some conclusions that may prove helpful in ameliorating the effects of future calamities of this sort. The increasing height of the successive waves was perhaps the most important lesson. We found that in some places the second or third waves were the largest, but elsewhere the seventh or eighth reached the greatest height. On the western coast of Hawaii (the big island) some waves actually came in during the following night after an interval of eighteen hours and reached heights greater than those experienced that morning. These surprising reports were confirmed by a considerable number of sources, but are not readily understood. It can only be supposed that the waves represented a reflection from a submarine cliff off Japan and another reflection from an escarpment in Oceania, so that finally the waves, after making what is comparable to a three-cushion shot in billiards, arrived at their destination. In any case the danger of possible late wave arrivals, especially on protected sides of islands, cannot be minimized.

About the most dangerous thing that a person can do during a tsunami is to walk out on the exposed reefs to gather up the fish left by the retreating seas. In 1946 many of the drownings in Hawaii occurred as a result of this activity, a natural reaction of people whose livelihood comes from the sea and who for the most part had never even heard of a tsunami (the last one of any size having occurred in 1877). The building of sea walls in front of a town, as had been done at Hilo, is helpful even if the sea wall is knocked over by the advancing waves. Undoubtedly the friction considerably decreases the power of the waves. Wherever possible the restriction of building to zones that have at least moderate elevation above sea level in danger areas is recommended.

In the tropics the corals have been very helpful in sparing man from even worse trouble from tsunamis by building large protective reefs along many coasts. The widest reef in the Hawaiian Islands, at Kaneohe Bay, is found on the north side of the Island of Oahu and therefore on the side from which the waves approached. Yet this wide reef seems to have been entirely effective in stopping the progress of the waves. Most people living in its lee were not even aware that a tsunami had occurred. Heights of not more than one or two feet were all that could be found by careful investigations along this shore. Other areas where reefs had smaller widths were less fortunate, as at Kawela Bay, where we were living behind a small reef and where the water rose 10 to 19 feet. However, the height of the raised water level, behind these reefs, was in almost every case less than in adjacent areas, where the water came in unimpeded.

Similarly, the existence of a submarine valley or canyon off a coast definitely has an important effect. Just as ordinary wind waves are small at the heads of submarine valleys, so also tsunamis are greatly reduced by the spreading of the energy as the waves move up the valleys at a faster rate than over the intervening ridges. Conversely, the waves traveling over a submarine ridge are particularly large. For example, there are three ridges extending down the slope on the north side of Kauai Island, and over these the waves attained their greatest heights. So if you live in Hawaii and want to live next to the beach, build your house behind a coral reef or look at a chart to see if there is a submarine valley out in front.

A few destructive tsunamis have occurred in localities where no great trench is known to exist. Among these are the waves that swept in on Lisbon in 1755, moving up the Tagus River and causing a very heavy loss of life. These followed a great earthquake with a center under the Atlantic some distance off the shore.

The most destructive waves of all time have been related to volcanic activity. In 1883, when Krakatoa blew off its head, a sudden engulfment occurred, setting up very unusual waves. These rolled in on the adjacent islands of Java and Sumatra and drowned tens of thousands of natives, rising, it is said, to heights of well over 100 feet. Curious reports came from these waves. They showed on the tide gauges all the way around the world, even in the English Channel. If these tide-gauge records indicated a tsunami actually coming from the Krakatoa engulfment, the waves must have been reflected from numerous submarine escarpments in order to have reached such a destination. The waves were recorded also in the Hawaiian Islands, although here the time of arrival does not agree with the time that one would predict for a wave traveling from Krakatoa to the Hawaiian Islands. The explanation is still in doubt.

It is disturbing to consider what would happen if a tsunami should come into a shore like Long Island, where some of the beaches have hundreds of thousands of bathers during a warm summer day. We have no records of dangerous waves coming in at these places. However, in the case of the 1929 Grand Banks earthquake, which wrecked a large part of the submarine cables going between our east coast cities and Europe, there had been no previous record of tsunamis in the area. The waves accompanying the Grand Banks earthquake moved in on Bruin Peninsula on the south coast of Newfoundland, rising to 15 feet. Such rises would, of course, sweep over most of the beaches along the exposed portion of the east coast. Let us hope that no new submarine faults come suddenly into being and send waves into this area. The effect would be almost as bad as that of a hydrogen bomb.

The term *tidal wave* has sometimes been used also to describe a rise in sea level that accompanies a hurricane. A *storm tide* seems to be a more acceptable term. In 1900 the sea rose about 15 feet at Galveston, Texas, and topped the sea wall, sweeping into the city and drowning six thousand people. A sea wall has now been constructed that will probably prevent any recurrence of this sort, but there are other cities less well protected and subject to dangerous waves. In 1938 a great hurricane moved up the east coast, quite contrary to the predictions that had been made by the meteorologists, and passed inland across Long Island.

The sea here rose also about 15 feet, killing six hundred people and causing tremendous amounts of damage to the beach property. It developed numerous new inlets in the beaches and changed the appearance of the coast until it was practically unrecognizable after the waves had stopped. Several other hurricanes, notably those of 1954 on the east coast and that of 1957 in western Louisiana, have produced similar inundations. A far worse catastrophe of this sort occurred at the head of the Bay of Bengal in 1737, when 300,000 people were drowned during a hurricane. The rises accompanying these great storm waves are not unlike tsunamis, except that the waves do not come in rhythmic succession. The rise may be quite as rapid, but the high water usually last a longer time, and recurrences are not particularly pronounced.

The damage caused by all of these rises of sea level is related only in part to the high water. In addition, the natural barriers to wind waves that exist along the shore and many of the artificial walls and jetties become less protective, so that the wind waves are superimposed upon the top of the sea-level rise and wreak their havoc at a new high level.

CHARTING AND USING THE GULF STREAM

by
Benjamin Franklin

The story of Benjamin Franklin, the young printer's devil who became one of America's greatest men, appears in every American history. Franklin was author, publisher, diplomat, and one of the leaders of the American Revolution. Had he devoted his entire life to science, he might have achieved great eminence in the field, for he had the gifts of observation and of wonder. Learning that ships on the passage to England from America often traveled much faster than their counterparts sailing westward, he had the curiosity to ask the reason, and discovered that western voyages were delayed by the eastward movement of the Gulf Stream. The simple solution was to avoid the current, but when this was pointed out to the Lords of the Admiralty, they disdained what they believed was a ridiculous Yankee notion. But Franklin persisted. He had the course of the Gulf Stream carefully charted and in so doing made a lasting contribution to navigation.

DISCOURSING with Captain Folger, a very intelligent mariner of the Island of Nantucket, in New England, concerning the long passages made by some ships bound from England to New York, I received from him the following information, viz.,

That the island in which he lives is inhabited chiefly by people concerned in the whale fishery, in which they employed near 150 sail of vessels; that the whales are found generally near the edges of the *Gulph Stream,* a strong current so called, which comes out of the Gulph of Florida, passing northeasterly along the coast of America, and then turning off most easterly, running at the rate of 4, 3½, 3, and 2½ miles an hour. That the whaling business leading these people to cruise along the edges of the stream in quest of whales, they are become better acquainted with the course, breadth, strength, and extent of the same, than those navigators can well be who only cross it in their voyages to and from America, that they have opportunities of discovering the strength of it when their boats are out in the pursuit of this fish, and happen to get into the stream while the ship is out of it, or out of the stream while the ship is in it, for then they are separated very fast, and would soon lose sight of each other if care were not taken in crossing the stream to and fro. They frequently in the same meet and speak with ships bound from England to New York, Virginia, &c. who have passages of 8, 9, and 10 weeks and are still far from land, and not likely to be in with it for some time, being engaged in that part of the stream that sets directly against them, and it is supposed that their fear of Cape Sable Shoals, George's Banks, or Nantucket Shoals, hath induced them to keep so far to the southward as unavoidable to engage them in the said Gulph Stream, which occasions the length of their voyage, since in a calm it carries them directly back, and tho' they may have fair winds, yet the current being 60 or 70 miles a day, is so much subtracted from the way they make thro' the water. At my request Captain Folger hath been so obliging as to mark for me on a chart the dimensions, course and swiftness of the Stream from its first coming out of the Gulph when it is narrowest and strongest, until it turns away to go to the southward of the Western Islands, where it is broader and weaker, and to give me withall some written directions whereby ships bound from the banks of Newfoundland to New York may avoid the said Stream; and yet be free of danger from the banks and shoals above mentioned. As I apprehend that such chart and directions may be of use to our packets in shortning their voyages, I send them to you, that if their Lordships should think fit, so much of the chart as is contained within the red lines may be engraved, and printed, together with the remarks, at the charge of the office; or at least the manuscript copies may be made of the same for the use of the packets. The expence of the former would not much exceed the latter and would besides be of general service.

Letter to Anthony Todd, 1769

The Birth of an Island

by
Rachel Carson

As we have discovered in previous pages, the depths of the ocean are the scene of ceaseless activity. Earthquakes, volcanoes, slides of sand and water are frequent occurrences; and the all-pervading waters carry their effects to distant shores. These cataclysms have still another effect. Like their counterparts on shore, they change the contours of the sea, opening chasms, flattening protuberances, raising islands. Many of these changes are only dimly understood, but we do have information about the effects of volcanic eruptions in the creation of islands. How this creation takes place is described in "The Birth of an Island," another chapter from Rachel Carson's The Sea Around Us.

Many a green isle needs must be
In the deep, wide sea . . . SHELLEY

MILLIONS of years ago, a volcano built a mountain on the floor of the Atlantic. In eruption after eruption, it pushed up a great pile of volcanic rock, until it had accumulated a mass 100 miles across at its base, reaching upward toward the surface of the sea. Finally its cone emerged as an island with an area of about 200 square miles. Thousands of years passed, and thousands of thousands. Eventually the waves of the Atlantic cut down the cone and reduced it to a shoal—all of it, that is, but a small fragment which remained above water. This fragment we know as Bermuda.

With variations, the life story of Bermuda has been repeated by almost every one of the islands that interrupt the watery expanses of the oceans far from land. For these isolated islands in the sea are fundamentally different from the continents. The major land masses and the ocean basins are today much as they have been throughout the greater part of geologic time. But islands are ephemeral, created today, destroyed tomorrow. With few exceptions, they are the result of the violent, explosive, earth-shaking eruptions of submarine volcanoes, working perhaps for millions of years to achieve their end. It is one of the paradoxes in the ways of earth and sea that a process seemingly so destructive, so catastrophic in nature, can result in an act of creation.

Islands have always fascinated the human mind.

Perhaps it is the instinctive response of man, the land animal, welcoming a brief intrusion of earth in the vast, overwhelming expanse of sea. Here in a great ocean basin, a thousand miles from the nearest continent, with miles of water under our vessel, we come upon an island. Our imaginations can follow its slopes down through darkening waters to where it rests on the sea floor. We wonder why and how it arose here in the midst of the ocean.

The birth of a volcanic island is an event marked by prolonged and violent travail: the forces of the earth striving to create, and all the forces of the sea opposing. The sea floor, where an island begins, is probably nowhere more than about 50 miles thick—a thin covering over the vast bulk of the earth. In it are deep cracks and fissures, the results of unequal cooling and shrinkage in past ages. Along such lines of weakness the molten lava from the earth's interior presses up and finally bursts forth into the sea. But a submarine volcano is different from a terrestrial eruption, where the lava, molten rocks, gases, and other ejecta are hurled into the air through an open crater. Here on the bottom of the ocean the volcano has resisting it all the weight of the ocean water above it. Despite the immense pressure of, it may be, two or three miles of sea water, the new volcanic cone builds upward toward the surface, in flow after flow of lava. Once within reach of the waves, its soft ash and tuff are violently attacked, and for a long period the potential island may remain a shoal, unable to emerge. But, eventually, in new eruptions, the cone is pushed up into the air and a rampart against the attacks of the waves is built of hardened lava.

Navigators' charts are marked with numerous, recently discovered submarine mountains. Many of these are the submerged remnants of the islands of a geologic yesterday. The same charts show islands that emerged from the sea at least 50 million years ago, and others that arose within our own memory. Among the undersea mountains marked on the charts may be the islands of tomorrow, which at this moment are forming, unseen, on the floor of the ocean and are growing upward toward its surface.

For the sea is by no means done with submarine eruptions; they occur fairly commonly, sometimes detected only by instruments, sometimes obvious to the most casual observer. Ships in volcanic zones may suddenly find themselves in violently disturbed water. There are heavy discharges of steam. The sea appears to bubble or boil in a furious turbulence. Fountains spring from its surface. Floating up from the deep, hidden places of the actual eruption come the bodies of fishes and other deep-sea creatures, and quantities of volanic ash and pumice.

One of the youngest of the large volcanic islands of the world is Ascension in the South Atlantic. During the Second World War the American airmen sang

If we don't find Ascension
Our wives will get a pension

this island being the only piece of dry land between the hump of Brazil and the bulge of Africa. It is a forbidding mass of cinders, in which the vents of no less than forty extinct volcanoes can be counted. It has not always been so barren, for its slopes have yielded the fossil remains of trees. What happened to the forests no one knows; the first men to explore the island, about the year 1500, found it treeless, and today it has no natural greenness except on its highest peak, known as Green Mountain.

In modern times we have never seen the birth of an island as large as Ascension. But now and then there is a report of a small island appearing where none was before. Perhaps a month, a year, five years later, the island has disappeared into the sea again. These are the little, stillborn islands, doomed to only a brief emergence above the sea.

About 1830 such an island suddenly appeared in the Mediterranean between Sicily and the coast of Africa, rising from 100-fathom depths after there had been signs of volcanic activity in the area. It was little more than a black cinder pile, perhaps 200 feet high. Waves, wind, and rain attacked it. Its soft and porous materials were easily eroded; its substance was rapidly eaten away and it sank beneath the sea. Now it is a shoal, marked on the charts as Graham's Reef.

Falcon Island, the tip of a volcano projecting above the Pacific nearly 2,000 miles east of Australia, suddenly disappeared in 1913. Thirteen years later, after violent eruptions in the vicinity, it as suddenly rose again above the surface and remained as a physical bit of the British Empire until 1949. Then it was reported by the Colonial Under Secretary to be missing again.

Almost from the moment of its creation, a volcanic island is foredoomed to destruction. It has in itself the seeds of its own dissolution, for new explosions, or landslides of the soft soil, may violently accelerate its disintegration. Whether the destruction of an island comes quickly or only after long ages of geologic time may also depend on external forces: the rains that wear away the loftiest of land mountains, the sea, and even man himself.

South Trinidad, or in the Portuguese spelling, "Ilha Trinidade," is an example of an island that has been sculptured into bizarre forms through centuries of weathering—an island in which the signs of dissolution are clearly apparent. This group of volcanic peaks lies in the open Atlantic, about a thousand miles northeast of Rio de Janeiro. E. F. Knight wrote in 1907 that Trinidad "is rotten throughout, its substance has been disintegrated by volcanic fires and by the action of water, so that it is everywhere tumbling to pieces." During an interval of nine years between Knight's visits, a whole mountainside had collapsed in a great landslide of broken rocks and volcanic debris.

Sometimes the disintegration takes abrupt and violent form. The greatest explosion of historic time was the literal evisceration of the island of Krakatoa. In 1680 there had been a premonitory eruption on this small island in Sunda Strait, between Java and Sumatra in the Netherlands Indies. Two hundred years later there had been a series of earthquakes. In the spring of 1883, smoke and steam began to ascend from fissures in the volcanic cone. The ground became noticeably warm, and warning rumblings and hissings came from the volcano. Then, on August 27, Krakatoa literally exploded. In an appalling series of eruptions, that lasted two days, the whole northern half of the cone was carried away. The sudden inrush of ocean water added the fury of superheated steam to the cauldron. When the inferno of white-hot lava, molten rock, steam, and smoke had finally subsided, the island that had stood 1,400 feet above the sea had become a cavity a thousand feet below sea level. Only along one edge of the former crater did a remnant of the island remain.

Krakatoa, in its destruction, became known to the entire world. The eruption gave rise to a 100-foot wave that wiped out villages along the Strait and killed people by tens of thousands. The wave was felt on the shores of the Indian Ocean and at Cape Horn; rounding the Cape into the Atlantic, it sped northward and retained its identity even as far as the English Channel. The sound of the explosions was heard in the Philippine Islands, in Australia, and on the Island of Madagascar, nearly 3,000 miles away. And clouds of volcanic dust, the pulverized rock that had been torn from the heart of Krakatoa, ascended into the stratosphere and were carried around the globe to give rise to a series of spectacular sunsets in every country of the world for nearly a year.

Although Krakatoa's dramatic passing was the most violent eruption that modern man has witnessed, Krakatoa itself seems to have been the product of an even greater one. There is evidence that an immense volcano once stood where the waters of Sunda Strait now lie. In some remote period a titanic explosion blew it away, leaving only its base represented by a broken ring of islands. The largest of these was Krakatoa, which, in its own demise, carried away what was left of the original crater ring. But in 1929 a new volcanic island arose in this place—Anak Krakatoa, Child of Krakatoa.

Subterranean fires and deep unrest disturb the whole area occupied by the Aleutians. The islands themselves are the peaks of a thousand-mile chain of undersea mountains, of which volcanic action was the chief architect. The geologic structure of the ridge is little known, but it rises abruptly from oceanic depths of about a mile on one side and two miles on the other. Apparently this long narrow ridge indicates a deep fracture of the earth's crust. On many of the islands volcanoes are now active, or only temporarily quiescent. In the short history of modern navigation in this region, it has often happened that a new island has been reported but perhaps only the following year could not be found.

The small island of Bogoslof, since it was first

observed in 1796, has altered its shape and position several times and has even disappeared completely, only to emerge again. The original island was a mass of black rock, sculptured into fantastic, tower-like shapes. Explorers and sealers coming upon it in the fog were reminded of a castle and named it Castle Rock. At the present time there remain only one or two pinnacles of the castle, a long spit of black rocks where sea lions haul out, and a cluster of higher rocks resounding with the cries of thousands of sea birds. Each time the parent volcano erupts, as it has done at least half a dozen times since men have been observing it, new masses of steaming rocks emerge from the heated waters, some to reach heights of several hundred feet before they are destroyed in fresh explosions. Each new cone that appears is, as described by the volcanologist Jaggar, "the live crest, equivalent to a crater, of a great submarine heap of lava 6,000 feet high, piled above the floor of Bering Sea where the Aleutian mountains fall off to the deep sea."

One of the few exceptions to the almost universal rule that oceanic islands have a volcanic origin seems to be the remarkable and fascinating group of islets known as the Rocks of St. Paul. Lying in the open Atlantic between Brazil and Africa, St. Paul's Rocks are an obstruction thrust up from the floor of the ocean into the midst of the racing Equatorial Current, a mass against which the seas, which have rolled a thousand miles unhindered, break in sudden violence. The entire cluster of rocks covers not more than a quarter of a mile, running in a curved line like a horseshoe. The highest rock is no more than 60 feet above the sea; spray wets it to the summit. Abruptly the rocks dip under water and slope steeply down into great depths. Geologists since the time of Darwin have puzzled over the origin of these black, wave-washed islets. Most of them agree that they are composed of material like that of the sea floor itself. In some remote period, inconceivable stresses in the earth's crust must have pushed a solid rock mass upward more than two miles.

So bare and desolate that not even a lichen grows on them, St. Paul's Rocks would seem one of the most unpromising places in the world to look for a spider, spinning its web in arachnidan hope of snaring passing insects. Yet Darwin found spiders when he visited the Rocks in 1833, and forty years later the naturalists of H.M.S. *Challenger* also reported them, busy at their web-spinning. A few insects are there, too, some as parasites on the sea birds, three species of which nest on the Rocks. One of the insects is a small brown moth that lives on feathers. This very nearly completes the inventory of the inhabitants of St. Paul's Rocks, except for the grotesque crabs that swarm over the islets, living chiefly on the flying fish brought by the birds to their young.

St. Paul's Rocks are not alone in having an extraordinary assortment of inhabitants, for the faunas and floras of oceanic islands are amazingly different from those of the continents. The pattern of island life is peculiar and significant. Aside from forms recently introduced by man, islands remote from the continents are never inhabited by any land mammals, except sometimes the one mammal that has learned to fly—the bat. There are never any frogs, salamanders, or other amphibians. Of reptiles, there may be a few snakes, lizards, and turtles, but the more remote the island from a major land mass, the fewer reptiles there are, and the really isolated islands have none. There are usually a few species of land birds, some insects, and some spiders. So remote an island as Tristan da Cunha in the South Atlantic, 1,500 miles from the nearest continent, has no land animals but these: three species of land birds, a few insects, and several small snails.

With so selective a list, it is hard to see how, as some biologists believe, the islands could have been colonized by migration across land bridges, even if there were good evidence for the existence of the bridges. The very animals missing from the islands are the ones that would have had to come dry-shod, over the hypothetical bridges. The plants and animals that we find on oceanic islands, on the other hand, are the ones that could have come by wind or water. As an alternative, then, we must suppose that the stocking of the islands has been accomplished by the strangest migration in earth's history—a migration that began long before man appeared on earth and is still continuing, a migration that seems more like a series of cosmic accidents than an orderly process of nature.

We can only guess how long after its emergence from the sea an oceanic island may lie uninhabited. Certainly in its original state it is a land bare, harsh, and repelling beyond human experience. No living thing moves over the slopes of its volcanic hills; no plants cover its naked lava fields. But little by little, riding on the winds, drifting on the currents, or rafting in on logs, floating brush, or trees, the plants and animals that are to colonize it arrive from the distant continents.

So deliberate, so unhurried, so inexorable are the ways of nature that the stocking of an island may require thousands or millions of years. It may be that no more than half a dozen times in all these eons does a particular form, such as a tortoise, make a successful landing upon its shores. To wonder impatiently why man is not a constant witness of such arrivals is to fail to understand the majestic pace of the process.

Yet we have occasional glimpses of the method. Natural rafts of uprooted trees and matted vegetation have frequently been seen adrift at sea, more than a thousand miles off the mouths of such great tropical rivers as the Congo, the Ganges, the Amazon, and the Orinoco. Such rafts could easily carry an assortment of insect, reptile, or mollusk passengers. Some of the involuntary passengers might be able to withstand long weeks at sea; others would die during the first stages of the journey. Probably the ones best adapted for travel by raft are the wood-boring insects, which, of all the insect tribe, are most commonly found on oceanic islands. The poorest raft travelers must be the mammals. But even a mammal might cover short interisland distances. A few days after the explosion of Krakatoa, a small monkey was rescued from some drifting timber in Sunda Strait. She had been terribly burned, but survived the experience.

No less than the water, the winds and the air currents play their part in bringing inhabitants to the islands. The upper atmosphere, even during the ages before man entered it in his machines, was a place of congested traffic. Thousands of feet above the earth, the air is crowded with living creatures, drifting, flying, gliding, ballooning, or involuntarily swirling along on the high winds. Discovery of this rich aerial plankton had to wait until man himself had found means to make physical invasion of these regions. With special nets and traps, scientists have now collected from the upper atmosphere many of the forms that inhabit oceanic islands. Spiders, whose almost invariable presence on these islands is a fascinating problem, have been captured nearly three miles above the earth's surface. Airmen have passed through great numbers of the white, silken filaments of spiders' "parachutes" at heights of two to three miles. At altitudes of 6,000 to 16,000 feet, and with wind velocities reaching 45 miles an hour, many living insects have been taken. At such heights and on such strong winds, they might well have been carried hundreds of miles. Seeds have been collected at altitudes up to 5,000 feet. Among those commonly taken are members of the Composite family, especially the so-called "thistledown" typical of oceanic islands.

An interesting point about transport of living plants and animals by wind is the fact that in the upper layers of the earth's atmosphere the winds do not necessarily blow in the same direction as at the earth's surface. The trade winds are notably shallow, so that a man standing on the cliffs of St. Helena, 1,000 feet above the sea, is above the wind, which blows with great force below him. Once drawn into the upper air, insects, seeds, and the like can easily be carried in a direction contrary to that of the winds prevailing at island level.

The wide-ranging birds that visit islands of the ocean in migration may also have a good deal to do with the distribution of plants, and perhaps even of some insects and minute land shells. From a ball of mud taken from a bird's plumage, Charles Darwin raised eighty-two separate plants, belonging to five distinct species! Many plant seeds have hooks or prickles, ideal for attachment to feathers. Such birds as the Pacific golden plover, which annually flies from the mainland of Alaska to the Hawaiian Islands and even beyond, probably figure in many riddles of plant distribution.

The catastrophe of Krakatoa gave naturalists a perfect opportunity to observe the colonization of an island. With most of the island itself destroyed, and the remnant covered with a deep layer of lava and ash that remained hot for weeks, Krakatoa after the explosive eruptions of 1883 was, from a biological standpoint, a new volcanic island. As soon as it was possible to visit it, scientists searched for signs of life, although it was hard to imagine how any living thing could have survived. Not a single plant or animal could be found. It was not until nine months after the eruption that the naturalist Cotteau was able to report: "I only discovered one microscopic spider—only one. This strange pioneer of the renovation was busy spinning its web." Since there were no insects on the island, the web-spinning of the bold little spider was presumably in vain, and, except for a few blades of grass, practically nothing lived on Krakatoa for a quarter of a century. Then the colonists began to arrive—a few mammals in 1908; a number of birds, lizards, and snakes; various mollusks, insects, and earthworms. Ninety per cent of Krakatoa's new inhabitants, Dutch scientists found, were forms that could have arrived by air.

Isolated from the great mass of life on the continents, with no opportunity for the crossbreeding that tends to preserve the average and to eliminate the new and unusual, island life has developed in a remarkable manner. On these remote bits of earth, nature has excelled in the creation of strange and wonderful forms. As though to prove her incredible versatility, almost every island has developed species that are endemic—that is, they are peculiar to it alone and are duplicated nowhere else on earth.

It was from the pages of earth's history written on

the lava fields of the Galápagos that young Charles Darwin got his first inkling of the great truths of the origin of species. Observing the strange plants and animals—giant tortoises, black, amazing lizards that hunted their food in the surf, sea lions, birds in extraordinary variety—Darwin was struck by their vague similarity to mainland species of South and Central America, yet was haunted by the differences, differences that distinguish them not only from the mainland species but from those on other islands of the archipelago. Years later he was to write in reminiscence: "Both in space and time, we seem to be brought somewhat near to that great fact—that mystery of mysteries—the first appearance of new beings on earth."

Of the "new beings" evolved on islands, some of the most striking examples have been birds. In some remote age before there were men, a small, pigeonlike bird found its way to the island of Mauritius, in the Indian Ocean. By processes of change at which we can only guess, this bird lost the power of flight, developed short, stout legs, and grew larger until it reached the size of a modern turkey. Such was the origin of the fabulous dodo, which did not long survive the advent of man on Mauritius. New Zealand was the sole home of the moas. One species of these ostrichlike birds stood 12 feet high. Moas had roamed New Zealand from the early part of the Tertiary; those that remained when the Maoris arrived soon died out.

Other island forms besides the dodo and the moas

have tended to become large. Perhaps the Galápagos tortoise became a giant after its arrival on the islands, although fossil remains on the continents cast doubt on this. The loss of wing use and even of the wings themselves (the moas had none) are common results of insular life. Insects on small, wind-swept islands tend to lose the power of flight—those that retain it are in danger of being blown out to sea. The Galápagos Islands have a flightless cormorant. There have been at least fourteen species of flightless rails on the islands of the Pacific alone.

One of the most interesting and engaging characteristics of island species is their extraordinary tameness—a lack of sophistication in dealings with the human race, which even the bitter teachings of experience do not quickly alter. When Robert Cushman Murphy visited the island of South Trinidad in 1913 with a party from the brig *Daisy*, terns alighted on the heads of the men in the whaleboat and peered inquiringly into their faces. Albatrosses on Laysan, whose habits include wonderful ceremonial dances, allowed naturalists to walk among their colonies and responded with a grave bow to similar polite greetings from the visitors. When the British ornithologist David Lack visited the Galápagos Islands, a century after Darwin, he found that the hawks allowed themselves to be touched, and the flycatchers tried to remove hair from the heads of the men for nesting material. "It is a curious pleasure," he wrote, "to have the birds of the wilderness settling upon one's shoulders, and the pleasure could be much less rare were man less destructive."

But man, unhappily, has written one of his blackest records as a destroyer on the oceanic islands. He has seldom set foot on an island that he has not brought about disastrous changes. He has destroyed environments by cutting, clearing, and burning; he has brought with him as a chance associate the nefarious rat; and almost invariably he has turned loose upon the islands a whole Noah's Ark of goats, hogs, cattle, dogs, cats, and other nonnative animals as well as plants. Upon species after species of island life, the black night of extinction has fallen.

In all the world of living things, it is doubtful whether there is a more delicately balanced relationship than that of island life to its environment. This environment is a remarkably uniform one. In the midst of a great ocean, ruled by currents and winds that rarely shift their course, climate changes little. There are few natural enemies, perhaps none at all. The harsh struggle for existence that is the normal lot of continental life is softened on the islands. When this gentle pattern of life is abruptly changed, the island creatures have little ability to make the adjustments necessary for survival.

Ernst Mayr tells of a steamer wrecked off Lord Howe Island east of Australia in 1918. Its rats swam ashore. In two years they had so nearly exterminated the native birds that an islander wrote, "This paradise of birds has become a wilderness, and the quietness of death reigns where all was melody."

On Tristan da Cunha almost all of the unique land birds that had evolved there in the course of the ages were exterminated by hogs and rats. The native fauna of the island of Tahiti is losing ground against the horde of alien species that man has introduced. The Hawaiian Islands, which have lost their native plants and animals faster than almost any other area in the world, are a classic example of the results of interfering with natural balances. Certain relations of animal to plant, and of plant to soil, had grown up through the centuries. When man came in and rudely disturbed this balance, he set off a whole series of chain reactions.

Vancouver brought cattle and goats to the Hawaiian Islands, and the resulting damage to forests and other vegetation was enormous. Many plant introductions were as bad. A plant known as the pamakani was brought in many years ago, according to report, by a Captain Makee for his beautiful gardens on the island of Maui. The pamakani, which has light, wind-borne seeds, quickly escaped from the captain's gardens, ruined the pasture lands on Maui, and proceeded to hop from island to island. The CCC boys were at one time put to work to clear it out of the Honouliuli Forest Reserve, but as fast as they destroyed it, the seeds of new plants arrived on the wind. Lantana was another plant brought in as an ornamental species.

Now it covers thousands of acres with a thorny, scrambling growth—despite large sums of money spent to import parasitic insects to control it.

There was once a society in Hawaii for the special purpose of introducing exotic birds. Today when you go to the islands you see, instead of the exquisite native birds that greeted Captain Cook, mynas from India, cardinals from the United States or Brazil, doves from Asia, weavers from Australia, skylarks from Europe, and titmice from Japan. Most of the original bird life has been wiped out, and to find its fugitive remnants you would have to search assiduously in the most remote hills.

Some of the island species have, at best, the most tenuous hold on life. The Laysan teal is found nowhere in the world but on the one small island of Laysan. Even on this island it occurs only on one end, where there is a seepage of fresh water. Probably the total population of this species does not exceed fifty individuals. Destruction of the small swampy bit of land that is its home, or the introduction of a hostile or competing species, could easily snap the slender thread of life.

Most of man's habitual tampering with nature's balance by introducing exotic species has been done in ignorance of the fatal chain of events that would follow. But in modern times, at least, we might profit by history. About the year 1513, the Portuguese introduced goats onto the recently discovered island of St. Helena, which had developed a magnificent forest of gumwood, ebony, and brazilwood. By 1560 or thereabouts, the goats had so multiplied that they wandered over the island by the thousand, in flocks a mile long. They trampled the young trees and ate the seedlings. By this time the colonists had begun to cut and burn the forests, so that it is hard to say whether men or goats were the more responsible for the destruction. But of the result there was no doubt. By the early 1800's the forests were gone, and the naturalist Alfred Wallace later described this once beautiful, forest-clad volcanic island as a "rocky desert," in which the remnants of the original flora persisted only in the most inaccessible peaks and crater ridges.

When the astronomer Halley visited the islands of the Atlantic about 1700, he put a few goats ashore on South Trinidad. This time, without the further aid of man, the work of deforestation proceeded so rapidly that it was nearly completed within the century. Today Trinidad's slopes are the place of a ghost forest, strewn with the fallen and decaying trunks of long-dead trees; its soft volcanic soils, no longer held by the interlacing roots, are sliding away into the sea.

One of the most interesting of the Pacific islands was Laysan, a tiny scrap of soil which is a far outrider of the Hawaiian chain. It once supported a forest of sandalwood and fanleaf palms and had five land birds, all peculiar to Laysan alone. One of them was the Laysan rail, a charming, gnomelike creature no more than six inches high, with wings that seemed too small (and were never used as wings), and feet that seemed too large, and a voice like distant, tinkling bells. About 1887, the captain of a visiting ship moved some of the rails to Midway, about 300 miles to the west, establishing a second colony. It seemed a fortunate move, for soon thereafter rabbits were introduced on Laysan. Within a quarter of a century, the rabbits had killed off the vegetation of the tiny island, reduced it to a sandy desert, and all but exterminated themselves. As for the rails the devastation of their island was fatal, and the last rail died about 1924.

Perhaps the Laysan colony could later have been restored from the Midway group had not tragedy struck there also. During the war in the Pacific, rats went ashore to island after island from ships and landing craft. They invaded Midway in 1943. The adult rails were slaughtered. The eggs were eaten, and the young birds killed. The world's last Laysan rail was seen in 1944.

The tragedy of the oceanic islands lies in the uniqueness, the irreplaceability of the species they have developed by the slow processes of the ages. In a reasonable world men would have treated these islands as precious possessions, as natural museums filled with beautiful and curious works of creation, valuable beyond price because nowhere in the world are they duplicated. W. H. Hudson's lament for the birds of the Argentine pampas might even more truly have been spoken of the islands: "The beautiful has vanished and returns not."

A Descent into the Maelstrom

by

Edgar Allan Poe

One of the most fascinating and horrifying short stories ever penned by an American is printed below. Many who read it will ask whether the incidents Poe recounts were a product of his own imagination or whether they were based in actual fact. It is true that to heighten the dramatic effect Poe exaggerates certain details, but no less an authority than Rachel Carson, author of two of the previous chapters in this book, vouches for the story's basic authenticity. There is a Maelstrom and it is located off the Norwegian coast where Poe places it. According to Miss Carson, it is "a gigantic whirlpool or series of whirlpools and men with their boats have been drawn down into the spinning funnels of water."

WE HAD now reached the summit of the loftiest crag. For some minutes the old man seemed too much exhausted to speak.

"Not long ago," said he at length, "and I could have guided you on this route as well as the youngest of my sons; but, about three years past, there happened to me an event such as never before happened to mortal man—or at least such as no man ever survived to tell of—and the six hours of deadly terror which I then endured have broken me up body and soul. You suppose me a *very* old man—but I am not. It took less than a single day to change these hairs from a jetty black to white, to weaken my limbs, and to unstring my nerves, so that I tremble at the least exertion, and am frightened at a shadow. Do you know that I can scarcely look over this little cliff without getting giddy?"

The "little cliff" upon whose edge he had so carelessly thrown himself down to rest that the weightier portion of his body hung over it, while he was only kept from falling by the tenure of his elbow on its extreme and slippery edge—this "little cliff" arose, a sheer unobstructed precipice of black shining rock, some fifteen or sixteen hundred feet from the world of crags beneath us. Nothing would have tempted me within half a dozen yards of its brink. In truth so deeply was I excited by the perilous position of my companion that I fell at full length upon the ground, clung to the shrubs around me, and dared not even glance upward at the sky—while I struggled in vain to divest myself of the idea that the very foundations of the mountain were in danger from the fury of the winds. It was long before I could reason myself into sufficient courage to sit up and look out into the distance.

"You must get over these fancies," said the guide, "for I have brought you here that you might have the best possible view of the scene of that event I mentioned—and to tell you the whole story with the spot just under your eye.

"We are now," he continued, in that particularizing manner which distinguished him—"we are now close upon the Norwegian coast—in the sixty-eighth degree of latitude—in the great province of Nordland—and in the dreary district of Lofoden. The mountain upon whose top we sit is Helseggen, the Cloudy. Now raise yourself up a little higher—hold on to the grass if you feel giddy—so—and look out, beyond the belt of vapor beneath us, into the sea."

I looked dizzily, and beheld a wide expanse of ocean, whose waters were so inky a hue as to bring at once to my mind the Nubian geographer's account of the *Mare Tenebrarum*. A panorama more deplorably desolate no human imagination can conceive. To the right and left, as far as the eye could reach, there lay outstretched, like ramparts of the world, lines of horridly black and beetling cliff, whose character of gloom was but the more forcibly illustrated by the surf which reared high up against it, its white and ghastly crest howling and shrieking forever. Just opposite the promontory upon whose apex we were placed, and at a distance of some five or six miles out at sea, there was visible a small, bleak-looking island; or, more properly, its position was discernible through the wilderness of surge in which it was enveloped. About two miles nearer the land arose another of smaller size, hideously craggy and barren, and encompassed at various intervals by a cluster of dark rocks.

The appearance of the ocean, in the space between the more distant island and the shore, had something very unusual about it. Although, at the time, so strong a gale was blowing landward that a brig in the remote offing lay to under a double-reefed trysail, and constantly plunged her whole hull out of sight, still there was here nothing like a regular swell, but only a short, quick, angry cross dashing of water in every direction —as well in the teeth of the wind as otherwise. Of foam there was little except in the immediate vicinity of the rocks.

"The island in the distance," resumed the old man, "is Moskoe. That a mile to the northward is Ambaaren. Yonder are Islesen, Hotholm, Keildhelm, Suarven, and Buckholm. Farther off—between Moskoe and Vurrgh—are Otterholm, Flimen, Sandflesen, and Stockholm. These are the true names of the places—but why it has been thought necessary to name them at all is more than either you or I can understand. Do you hear anything? Do you see any change in the water?"

We had now been about ten minutes upon the top

of Helseggen, to which we had ascended from the interior of Lofoden, so that we had caught no glimpse of the sea until it had burst upon us from the summit. As the old man spoke I became aware of a loud and gradually increasing sound, like the moaning of a vast herd of buffaloes upon an American prairie; and at the same moment I perceived that what seamen term the "chopping" character of the ocean beneath us was rapidly changing into a current which set to the eastward. Even while I gazed, this current acquired a monstrous velocity. Each moment added to its speed —to its headlong impetuosity. In five minutes the whole sea, as far as Vurrgh, was lashed into ungovernable fury; but it was between Moskoe and the coast that the main uproar held its sway. Here the vast bed of the waters, seamed and scarred into a thousand conflicting channels, burst suddenly into frenzied convulsion—heaving, boiling, hissing—gyrating in gigantic and innumerable vortices, and all whirling and plunging on to the eastward with a rapidity which water never elsewhere assumes, except in precipitous descents.

In a few minutes more, there came over the scene another radical alteration. The general surface grew somewhat more smooth, and the whirlpools, one by one, disappeared, while prodigious streaks of foam became apparent where none had been seen before. These streaks, at length, spreading out to a great distance, and entering into combination, took unto themselves the gyratory motion of the subsided vortices, and seemed to form the germ of another more vast. Suddenly—very suddenly—this assumed a distinct and definite existence, in a circle of more than a mile in diameter. The edge of the whirl was represented by a broad belt of gleaming spray; but no particle of this slipped into the mouth of the terrific funnel, whose interior, as far as the eye could fathom it, was a smooth, shining, and jet-black wall of water, inclined to the horizon at an angle of some forty-five degrees, speeding dizzily round and round with a swaying and sweltering motion, and sending forth to the winds an appalling voice, half shriek, half roar, such as not even the mighty cataract of Niagara ever lifts up in its agony to heaven.

The mountain trembled to its very base, and the rock rocked. I threw myself upon my face, and clung to the scant herbage in an excess of nervous agitation.

"This," said I at length, to the old man—"this *can* be nothing else but the great whirlpool of the Maelstrom."

"So it is sometimes termed," said he. "We Norwegians call it the Moskoe-strom, from the island of Moskoe in the midway."

The ordinary account of this vortex had by no means prepared me for what I saw. That of Jonas Ramus, which is perhaps the most circumstantial of any, cannot impart the faintest conception either of the magnificence or of the horror of the scene—or of the wild bewildering sense of *the novel* which confounds the beholder. I am not sure from what point of view the writer in question surveyed it, nor at what time, but it could neither have been from the summit of Helseggen nor during a storm. There are some passages of his description, nevertheless, which may be quoted for their details, although their effect is exceedingly feeble in conveying an impression of the spectacle.

"Between Lofoden and Moskoe," he says, "the depth of the water is between thirty-six and forty fathoms; but on the other side, toward Ver (Vurrgh) this depth decreases so as not to afford a convenient passage for a vessel, without the risk of splitting on the rocks, which happens even in the calmest weather. When it is flood, the stream runs up the country between Lofoden and Moskoe with a boisterous rapidity; but the roar of its impetuous ebb to the sea is scarce equalled by the loudest and most dreadful cataracts; the noise being heard several leagues off, and the vortices or pits are of such an extent and depth, that if a ship comes within its attraction, it is inevitably absorbed and carried down to the bottom, and there beat to pieces against the rocks; and when the water relaxes, the fragments thereof are thrown up again. But these intervals of tranquillity are only at the turn of the ebb and flood, and in calm weather, and last but a quarter of an hour, its violence gradually returning. When the stream is most boisterous, and its fury heightened by a storm, it is dangerous to come within a Norway mile of it. Boats, yachts, and ships have been carried away by not guarding against it before they were carried within its reach. It likewise happens frequently that whales come too near the stream, and are overpowered by its violence; and then it is impossible to describe their howlings and bellowings in their fruitless struggles to disengage themselves. A bear once, in attempting to swim from Lofoden to Moskoe, was caught by the stream and borne down, while he roared terribly, so as to be heard on shore. Large stocks of firs and pine-trees, after being absorbed by the current, rise again broken and torn to such a degree as if bristles grew upon them. This plainly shows the bottom to consist of craggy rocks, among which they are whirled to and fro. This stream is regulated by the flux and reflux of the sea—it being constantly high and low water every six hours. In the year 1645, early in the morning of Sexagesima Sunday, it raged with such a noise and impetuosity that the very stones of the houses on the coast fell to the ground."

In regard to the depth of the water, I could not see how this could have been ascertained at all in the immediate vicinity of the vortex. The "forty fathoms" must have reference only to portions of the channel close upon the shore of either Moskoe or Lofoden. The depth in the middle of the Moskoe-strom must be unmeasurably greater; and no better proof of this fact is necessary than can be obtained from even the sidelong glance into the abyss of the whirl which may be had from the highest crag of Helseggen. Looking down from this pinnacle upon the howling Phlegethon below, I could not help smiling at the simplicity with which the honest Jonas Ramus records, as a matter difficult of belief, the anecdotes of the whales and the bears, for it appeared to me, in fact, a self-evident thing that the largest ships of the line in existence, coming within the influence of that deadly attraction, could resist it as little as a feather the hurricane, and must disappear bodily at once.

The attempts to account for the phenomenon—some of which I remember, seemed to me sufficiently plausible in perusal—now wore a very different and unsatisfactory aspect. The idea generally received is that this, as well as three smaller vortices among the Ferroe Islands, "have no other cause than the collision of waves rising and falling, at flux and reflux, against a ridge of rocks and shelves, which confines the water so that it precipitates itself like a cataract; and thus the higher the flood rises, the deeper the fall must be, and the natural result of all is a whirlpool or vortex, the prodigious suction of which is sufficiently known by lesser experiments." These are the words of the *Encyclopædia Britannica*. Kircher and others imagine that in the center of the channel of the Maelstrom is an abyss penetrating the globe, and issuing in some very remote part—the Gulf of Bothnia being somewhat decidedly named in one instance. This opinion, idle in itself, was the one to which, as I gazed, my imagination most readily assented; and mentioning it to the guide, I was rather surprised to hear him say that although it was the view almost universally entertained of the subject by the Norwegians, it nevertheless was not his own. As to the former notion, he confessed his inability to comprehend it; and here I agreed with him—for, however conclusive on paper, it becomes altogether unintelligible, and even absurd, amid the thunder of the abyss.

"You have had a good look at the whirl now," said the old man, "and if you will creep round this crag, so as to get in its lee, and deaden the roar of the water, I will tell you a story that will convince you I ought to know something of the Moskoe-strom.

I placed myself as desired, and he proceeded.

"Myself and my two brothers once owned a schooner-rigged smack of about seventy tons burthen, with which we were in the habit of fishing among the islands beyond Moskoe, nearly to Vurrgh. In all violent eddies at sea there is good fishing at proper opportunities, if one has only the courage to attempt it; but among the whole of the Lofoden coastmen, we three were the only ones who made a regular business of going out to the islands, as I tell you. The usual grounds are a great way down to the southward. There fish can be got at all hours, without much risk, and therefore these places were preferred. The choice spots over here among the rocks, however, not only yield the finest variety, but in far greater abundance; so that we often got in a single day what the more timid of the craft could not scrape together in a week.

In fact, we made it a matter of desperate speculation—the risk of life standing instead of labor, and courage answering for capital.

"We kept the smack in a cove about five miles higher up the coast than this; and it was our practice, in fine weather, to take advantage of the fifteen minutes' slack to push across the main channel of the Moskoe-strom, far above the pool, and then drop down upon anchorage somewhere near Otterholm, or Sandflesen, where the eddies are not so violent as elsewhere. Here we used to remain until nearly time for slack water again, when we weighed and made for home. We never set out upon this expedition without a steady side wind for coming and going—one that we felt sure would not fail us before our return—and we seldom made a miscalculation upon this point. Twice, during six years, we were forced to stay all night at anchor on account of a dead calm, which is a rare thing indeed just about here; and once we had to remain on the grounds nearly a week, starving to death, owing to a gale which blew up shortly after our arrival, and made the channel too boisterous to be thought of. Upon this occasion we should have been driven out to sea in spite of everything (for the whirlpools threw us round and round so violently that, at length, we fouled our anchor and dragged it) if it had not been that we drifted into one of the innumerable cross-currents—here today and gone tomorrow—which drove us under the lee of Flimen, where, by good luck, we brought up.

"I could not tell you the twentieth part of the difficulties we encountered 'on the ground'—it is a bad spot to be in even in good weather—but we made shift always to run the gauntlet of the Moskoe-strom itself without accident; although at times my heart has been in my mouth when we happened to be a minute or so behind or before the slack. The wind sometimes was not as strong as we thought it at starting, and then we made rather less way than we could wish, while the current rendered the smack unmanageable. My eldest brother had a son eighteen years old, and I had two stout boys of my own. These would have been of great assistance at such times, in using the sweeps as well as afterward in fishing—but, somehow, although we ran the risk ourselves, we had not the heart to let the young ones get into danger—for, after all said and done, it *was* a horrible danger, and that is the truth.

"It is now within a few days of three years since what I am going to tell you occurred. It was on the tenth of July, 18—, a day which the people of this part of the world will never forget—for it was one in which blew the most terrible hurricane that ever came out of the heavens. And yet all the morning, and indeed until late in the afternoon, there was a gentle and steady breeze from the southwest, while the sun shone brightly, so that the oldest seaman among us could not have foreseen what was to follow.

"The three of us—my two brothers and myself—had crossed over to the islands about two o'clock P.M., and soon nearly loaded the smack with fine fish, which, we all remarked were more plenty that day than we had ever known them. It was just seven, *by my watch*, when we weighed and started for home, so as to make the worst of the Strom at slack water, which we knew would be at eight.

"We set out with a fresh wind on our starboard quarter, and for some time spanked along at a great rate, never dreaming of danger, for indeed we saw not the slightest reason to apprehend it. All at once we were taken aback by a breeze from over Helseggen. This was most unusual—something that had never happened to us before—and I began to feel a little uneasy, without exactly knowing why. We put the boat on the wind, but could make no headway at all for the eddies, and I was upon the point of proposing to return to the anchorage, when, looking astern, we saw the whole horizon covered with a singular copper-colored cloud that rose with the most amazing velocity.

"In the meantime the breeze that had headed us off fell away and we were dead becalmed, drifting about in every direction. This state of things, however, did not last long enough to give us time to think about it. In less than a minute the storm was upon us—in less than two the sky was entirely overcast—and what with this and the driving spray, it become suddenly so dark that we could not see each other in the smack.

"Such a hurricane as then blew it is folly to attempt describing. The oldest seaman in Norway never experienced anything like it. We had to let our sails go by the run before it cleverly took us; but, at the first puff, both our masts went by the board as if they had been sawed off—the mainmast taking with it my youngest brother who had lashed himself to it for safety.

"Our boat was the lightest feather of a thing that ever sat upon water. It had a complete flush deck, with only a small hatch near the bow, and this hatch it had always been our custom to batten down when about to cross the Strom, by way of precaution against the chopping seas. But for this circumstance we should have foundered at once—for we lay entirely buried for some moments. How my eldest brother escaped destruction I cannot say, for I never had an opportunity of ascertaining. For my part, as soon as I had let the foresail run, I threw myself flat on deck, with my feet against the narrow gunwale of the bow, and with my hands grasping a ring-bolt near the foot of the foremast. It was mere instinct that prompted me to do this—which was undoubtedly the best thing I could have done—for I was much too flurried to think.

"For some moments we were completely deluged, as I say, and all this time I held my breath, and clung to the bolt. When I could stand it no longer, I raised myself upon my knees, still keeping hold with my hands and thus got my head clear. Presently our little boat gave herself a shake just as a dog does in coming out of the water, and thus rid herself, in some measure, of the seas. I was now trying to get the better of the stupor that had come over me, and to collect my senses so as to see what was to be done, when I felt somebody grasp my arm. It was my eldest brother, and my heart leaped for joy, for I had made sure that he was overboard—but the next moment all this joy was turned to horror—for he put his mouth close to my ear, and screamed out the word, '*Moskoe-strom!*'

"No one will ever know what my feelings were at that moment. I shook from head to foot as if I had had the most violent fit of ague. I knew what he meant by that one word well enough—I knew what he wished to make me understand. With the wind that now drove us on, we were bound for the whirl of the Strom, and nothing could save us.

"You perceive that in crossing the Strom *channel*, we always went a long way up above the whirl, even in the calmest weather, and then had to wait and watch carefully for the slack—but now we were driving right upon the pool itself, and in such a hurricane as this! 'To be sure,' I thought, 'we shall get there just about the slack—there is some little hope in that'—but in the next moment I cursed myself for being so great a fool as to dream of hope at all. I knew very well that we were doomed, had we been ten times a ninety-gun ship.

"By this time the first fury of the tempest had spent itself, or perhaps we did not feel it so much, as we scudded before it, but at all events the seas, which at first had been kept down by the wind, and lay flat and frothing, now got up into absolute mountains. A singular change, too, had come over the heavens. Around in every direction it was still as black as pitch, but nearly overhead there burst out, all at once, a circular rift of clear sky—as clear as I ever saw—and of a deep bright blue—and through it there blazed forth the full moon with a luster that I never before knew her to wear. She lit up everything about us with the greatest distinctness—but, oh God, what a scene it was to light up!

"I now made one or two attempts to speak to my brother—but in some manner which I could not understand, the din had so increased that I could not make him hear a single word, although I screamed at the top of my voice in his ear. Presently he shook his head, looking as pale as death, and held up one of his fingers, as if to say, 'Listen!'

"At first I could not make out what he meant—but soon a hideous thought flashed upon me. I dragged my watch from its fob. It was not going. I glanced at its face in the moonlight and then burst into tears as I flung it far away into the ocean. *It had run down at seven o'clock! We were behind the time of the slack and the whirl of the Strom was in full fury!*

"When a boat is well built, properly trimmed, and not deep laden, the waves in a strong gale, when she is going large, seem always to slip from beneath her—which appears strange to a landsman, and this is what is called *riding,* in sea phrase.

"Well, so far we had ridden the waves very cleverly; but presently a gigantic sea happened to take us right under the counter, and bore us with it as it rose—

up—up—as if into the sky. I would not have believed that any wave could rise so high. And then down we came with a sweep, a slide, and a plunge that made me feel sick and dizzy, as if I was falling from some lofty mountain top in a dream. But while we were up I had thrown a quick glance around—and that one glance was all-sufficient. I saw our exact position in an instant. The Moskoe-strom whirlpool was about a quarter of a mile dead ahead—but no more like the everyday Moskoe-strom than the whirl, as you now see it, is like a mill race. If I had not known where we were and what we had to expect, I should not have recognized the place at all. As it was, I involuntarily closed my eyes in horror. The lids clenched themselves together as if in a spasm.

"It could not have been more than two minutes afterward until we suddenly felt the waves subside and were enveloped in foam. The boat made a sharp half-turn to larboard, and then shot off in its new direction like a thunderbolt. At the same moment the roaring noise of the water was completely drowned in a kind of shrill shriek—such a sound as you might imagine given out by the water pipes of many thousand steam vessels letting off their steam all together. We were now in the belt of surf that always surrounds the whirl; and I thought, of course, that another moment would plunge us into the abyss, down which we could only see indistinctly on account of the amazing velocity with which we were borne along. The boat did not seem to sink into the water at all, but to skim like an air bubble upon the surface of the surge. Her starboard side was next the whirl, and on the larboard arose the world of ocean we had left. It stood like a huge writhing wall between us and the horizon.

"It may appear strange, but now, when we were in the very jaws of the gulf, I felt more composed than when we were only approaching it. Having made up my mind to hope no more, I got rid of a great deal of that terror which unmanned me at first. I supposed it was despair that strung my nerves.

"It may look like boasting—but what I tell you is the truth—I began to reflect how magnificent a thing it was to die in such a manner, and how foolish it was in me to think of so paltry a consideration as my own individual life, in view of so wonderful a manifestation of God's power. I do believe that I blushed with shame when this idea crossed my mind. After a little while I became possessed with the keenest curiosity about the whirl itself. I positively felt a *wish* to explore its depths, even at the sacrifice I was going to make; and my principal grief was that I should never be able to tell my old companions on shore about the mysteries I should see. These, no doubt, were singular fancies to occupy a man's mind in such extremity—and I have often thought since that the revolutions of the boat around the pool might have rendered me a little lightheaded.

"There was another circumstance which tended to restore my self-possession; and this was the cessation of the wind, which could not reach us in our present position—for, as you saw for yourself, the belt of the surf is considerably lower than the general bed of the ocean, and this latter now towered above us, a high, black, mountainous ridge. If you have never been at sea in a heavy gale, you can form no idea of the confusion of mind occasioned by the wind and spray together. They blind, deafen, and strangle you, and take away all power of action or reflection. But we were now, in a great measure, rid of these annoyances—just as death-condemned felons in prison are allowed petty indulgences, forbidden them while their doom is yet uncertain.

"How often we made the circuit of the belt it is impossible to say. We careered round and round for perhaps an hour, flying rather than floating, getting gradually more and more into the middle of the surge, and then nearer and nearer to its horrible inner edge. All this time I had never let go of the ring-bolt. My brother was at the stern, holding on to a small empty water cask which had been securely lashed under the coop of the counter, and was the only thing on deck that had not been swept overboard when the gale first took us. As we approached the brink of the pit he let go his hold upon this and made for the ring, from which, in the agony of his terror, he endeavored to force my hands, as it was not large enough to afford us both a secure grasp. I never felt deeper grief than when I saw him attempt this act—although I knew he was a madman when he did it—a raving maniac through sheer fright. I did not care, however, to contest the point with him. I knew it could make no difference whether either of us held on at all; so I let him have the bolt, and went astern to the cask. This there was no great difficulty in doing; for the smack flew round steadily enough, and upon an even keel—only swaying to and fro with the immense sweeps and swelters of the whirl. Scarcely had I secured myself in my new position, when we gave a wild lurch to starboard, and rushed headlong into the abyss. I muttered a hurried prayer to God and thought all was over.

"As I felt the sickening sweep of the descent, I had instinctively tightened my hold upon the barrel and closed my eyes. For some seconds I dared not open them—while I expected instant destruction, and wondered that I was not already in my death struggles with the water. But moment after moment elapsed. I still lived. The sense of falling had ceased; and the motion of the vessel seemed much as it had been before, while in the belt of foam, with the exception that she now lay more along. I took courage and looked once again upon the scene.

"Never shall I forget the sensation of awe, horror, and admiration with which I gazed about me. The boat appeared to be hanging, as if by magic, midway down upon the interior surface of a funnel vast in circumference, prodigious in depth, and whose perfectly smooth sides might have been mistaken for ebony, but for the bewildering rapidity with which they spun round, and for the gleaming and ghastly radiance they shot forth, as the rays of the full moon, from that circular rift amid the clouds which I have already described, streamed in a flood of golden glory along the black walls and far away down into the inmost recesses of the abyss.

"At first I was too much confused to observe anything accurately. The general burst of terrific grandeur was all that I beheld. When I recovered myself a little, however, my gaze fell instinctively downward. In this direction I was able to obtain an unobstructed view, from the manner in which the smack hung on the inclined surface of the pool. She was quite upon an even keel—that is to say, her deck lay in a plane parallel with that of the water—but this latter sloped at an angle of more than forty-five degrees, so that we seemed to be lying upon our beam ends. I could not help observing, nevertheless, that I had scarcely more difficulty in maintaining my hold and footing in this situation than if we had been upon a dead level; and this I suppose was owing to the speed at which we revolved.

"The rays of the moon seemed to search to the very bottom of the profound gulf; but still I could make out nothing distinctly on account of a thick mist in which everything there was enveloped, and over which there hung a magnificent rainbow, like that narrow and tottering bridge which Mussulmans say is the only pathway between Time and Eternity. This mist, or spray, was no doubt occasioned by the clashing of the great walls of the funnel, as they all met together at the bottom—but the yell that went up to the heavens from out of that mist I dare not attempt to describe.

"Our first slide into the abyss itself, from the belt of foam above, had carried us a great distance down the slope; but our further descent was by no means proportionate. Round and round we swept—not with any uniform movement—but in dizzying swings and jerks, that sent us sometimes only a few hundred yards—sometimes nearly the complete circuit of the whirl. Our progress downward, at each revolution, was slow, but very perceptible!

"Looking about me upon the wide waste of liquid ebony on which we were thus borne, I perceived that our boat was not the only object in the embrace of the whirl. Both above and below us were visible fragments of vessels, large masses of building timber and trunks of trees, with many smaller articles, such as pieces of house furniture, broken boxes, barrels and staves. I have already described the unnatural curiosity which had taken the place of my original terrors. It appeared to grow upon me as I drew nearer and nearer to my dreadful doom. I now began to watch, with a strange interest, the numerous things that floated in our company. I *must* have been delirious, for I even sought *amusement* in speculating upon the relative velocities of their several descents toward the foam below. 'This fir tree,' I found myself at one time saying, 'will certainly be the next thing that takes the awful plunge and disappears'—and then I was disappointed to find that the wreck of a Dutch merchant ship overtook it and went down before. At length, after making several guesses of this nature, and being deceived in all, this fact—the fact of my invariable miscalculation—set me upon a train of reflection that made my limbs again tremble, and my heart beat heavily once more.

"It was not a new terror that thus affected me, but the dawn of a more exciting *hope*. This hope arose partly from memory and partly from present observation. I called to mind the great variety of buoyant matter that strewed the coast of Lofoden, having been absorbed and then thrown forth by the Moskoe-strom. By far the greater number of the articles were shattered in the most extraordinary way—so chafed and roughened as to have the appearance of being stuck full of splinters—but then I distinctly recollected that there were *some* of them which were not disfigured at all. Now I could not account for this difference except by supposing that the roughened fragments were the only ones which had been *completely absorbed*—that the others had entered into the whirl at so late a period of the tide, or, from some reason, had descended so slowly after entering that they did not reach the bottom before the turn of the flood came, or of the ebb, as the case might be. I conceived it possible, in either instance, that they might thus be whirled up again to the level of the ocean, without undergoing the fate of those which had been drawn in more early or absorbed more rapidly. I made, also, three important observations. The first was that, as a general rule, the larger the bodies were, the more rapid their descent—the second, that between two masses of equal extent, the one spherical and the other *of any other shape*, the superiority in speed of descent was with the sphere—the third, that between two masses of equal size, the one cylindrical and the other of any other shape, the cylinder was absorbed more slowly. Since my escape, I have had several conversations on this subject with an old schoolmaster in the district; and it was from him that I learned the use of the words 'cylinder' and 'sphere.' He explained to me—although I have forgotten the explanation—how what I observed was, in fact, the natural consequence of the forms of the floating fragments—and showed me how it happened that a cylinder, swimming in a vortex, offered more resistance to its suction, and was drawn in with greater difficulty, than an equally bulky body of any form whatever.

"There was one startling circumstance which went a great way in enforcing these observations, and rendering me anxious to turn them to account, and this was that at every revolution we passed something like a barrel, or else the yard or the mast of a vessel, while many of these things, which had been on our level when I first opened my eyes upon the wonders of the whirlpool, were now high up above us, and seemed to have moved but little from their original station.

"I no longer hesitated what to do. I resolved to lash myself securely to the water cask upon which I now held, to cut it loose from the counter, and to throw myself with it into the water. I attracted my brother's attention by signs, pointed to the floating barrels that came near us, and did everything in my power to make him understand what I was about to do. I thought at length that he comprehended my design—but, whether this was the case or not, he shook his head despairingly and refused to move from his station by the ring-bolt. It was impossible to reach him; the emergency admitted of no delay; and so, with a bitter struggle, I resigned him to his fate, fastened myself upon the cask by means of the lashings which secured it to the counter, and precipitated myself with it into the sea without another moment's hesitation.

"The result was precisely what I had hoped it might be. As it is myself who now tell you this tale—as you see that I did escape—and as you are already in possession of the mode in which this escape was effected, and must therefore anticipate all that I have farther to say—I will bring my story quickly to conclusion. It might have been an hour, or thereabout, after my quitting the smack, when, having descended to a vast distance beneath me, it made three or four wild gyrations in rapid succession, and, bearing my beloved brother with it, plunged headlong, at once and forever, into the chaos of foam below. The barrel to which I was attached sunk very little farther than half the distance between the bottom of the gulf and the spot at which I leaped overboard, before a great change took place in the character of the whirlpool. The slope of the sides of the vast funnel became momently less and less steep. The gyrations of the whirl grew, gradually, less and less violent. By degrees, the froth and the rainbow disappeared, and the bottom of the gulf seemed slowly to uprise. The sky was clear, the winds had gone down and the full moon was setting radiantly in the west, when I found myself on the surface of the ocean, in full view of the shores of Lofoden, and above the spot where the pool of the Moskoe-strom *had been*. It was the hour of the slack —but the sea still heaved in mountainous waves from the effects of the hurricane. I was borne violently into the channel of the Strom, and in a few minutes was hurried down the coast into the grounds of the fishermen. A boat picked me up—exhausted from fatigue—and (now that the danger was removed) speechless from the memory of its horror. Those who drew me on board were my old mates and daily companions—but they knew me no more than they would have known a traveler from the spirit land. My hair which had been raven-black the day before, was white as you see it now. They say too that the whole expression of my countenance had changed. I told them my story—they did not believe it. I now tell it to *you*—and I can scarcely expect you to put more faith in it than did the merry fishermen of Lofoden."

About the Editors

HELEN WRIGHT is an astronomer and writer. She studied at private schools in the United States and Switzerland and was graduated from Bennett Junior College and Vassar College where she was granted a B.A. and M.A. in astronomy.

Miss Wright has worked at the Vassar College Observatory, the Maria Mitchell Observatory, Mount Wilson and Palomar Observatories, and the United States Naval Observatory. She is a member of the American Astronomical Society and the History of Science Society.

She is the author of SWEEPER IN THE SKY—A LIFE OF MARIA MITCHELL; PALOMAR—THE WORLD'S LARGEST TELESCOPE; and EXPLORER OF THE UNIVERSE, A BIOGRAPHY OF GEORGE ELLERY HALE. With Harlow Shapley and Samuel Rapport she edited THE NEW TREASURY OF SCIENCE. She and Mr. Rapport are also editors of GREAT ADVENTURES IN SCIENCE, THE CRUST OF THE EARTH, THE GREAT EXPLORERS, GREAT ADVENTURES IN NURSING, THE AMAZING WORLD OF MEDICINE, and THE NEW YORK UNIVERSITY LIBRARY OF SCIENCE.

SAMUEL RAPPORT, a publisher by profession, was graduated from Cambridge Latin School and Harvard University. He is a vice-president of the publishing firm of Appleton-Century-Crofts.

Format by Kohar Alexanian
Set in Linotype Electra
Composed, printed and bound by American Book–Stratford Press, Inc.
HARPER & ROW, PUBLISHERS, INCORPORATED